ANTIQUES
and where to find them

Scotland

Compiled by
Loudon Temple

Paperback original published in Scotland
1 • 9 • 9 • 4

Antiques & Collectors' Guides Ltd.
Tel: 041 889 2063
© All rights reserved.

ISBN 0 9514842 3 0

Printed by Bell and Bain Ltd., Glasgow

Contents

Three attractive old photographs from the late 19th Century. Such finds can turn up in most antique shops and some second hand book shops in Scotland.

ollectors are a rare and fascinating breed, all with wide and varied interests. In America one group treasures the nasty little jaggy bits on sections of barbed wire from the days when individual makers had their own distinct way of twisting the strands into place. Recently, I met a man with a macabre fascination for obsolete dental instruments and another individual who has a house full of glass and ceramic insulator cups from telegraph poles and electricity pylons. Plastic phone cards have come on to the scene to be added to the list of trends with a worldwide following, and with thimble guilds, railway clubs, muzzle loaders associations and playing card societies to name but a few, there can be little doubt that everyone with an interest - no matter how bizarre - will find someone else out there in pursuit of the similar items.

I was smitten by the collecting bug as a youth in the 1950s when I first began to amass cards which were given away inside packets of Brooke Bond tea. I well remember trying to encourage my mother, grandmother and a number of aunts to change over to that brand and hopefully buy - and open - more than one packet at a time to help me on my quest to fill every last space in the little booklet provided.

Since those far off days, I have gone through many phases, attracted by Clarice Cliff pottery, '50s kitsch, Victorian postcards showing street scenes of my home town, Selkirk, Buchan pottery jugs, '30s silk hankies and plastic and tinplate toy robots from the 1950s and '60s .

Today, my passion is for the wonderful wood engravings of William Armour and fine quality early photographs, particularly if they have a Scottish interest. I also love the work of some modern glassblowers and like to believe that one day I may possess a few paintings by the remarkable Edinburgh artist Gordon K. Mitchell before they are all snapped up by art connoisseurs around the world.

Scotland in the 1990s has much to offer both the serious collector and those who are out for a spot of nothing-too-expensive browsing around.

There are hundreds of antiques shops, galleries, specialist outlets and auction rooms all over the country to cater for every taste or requirement and in this book we hope to guide those unfamiliar with what's on offer, through the city streets, town haunts and village by-ways where rich pickings are to be found. Antiques, record, postcard, toy and book fairs are also staged regularly in most of the bigger towns and cities. And those in need of a specialist craftsman will find the cream of the crop in the pages which follow.

Although every single antique shop, specialist dealership or auctioneer in the country is not to be found listed here, we guarantee that those who have participated in the publication - Scotland's first ever comprehensive guide for collectors - do take their business seriously. We have enjoyed visiting their premises. In the main, they are a friendly bunch who value their customers and will welcome private buyers and the trade with warm greetings and a firm intention to give service with a smile.

If readers have half as much enjoyment following our suggested outings as we had compiling this volume, we will feel quietly satisfied. Happy Hunting!

Loudon Temple.

Moffat photographer J.Weir took this charming study of four local likely lads in the 1870s.

A walnut Bureau of Lorimer Design (1918) and made by Whytock & Reid of Edinburgh, which attracted a top bid of £2,200 when sold by Christie's.

ravel to any one of the Scottish Border towns during the months of June and July and you will be transported back in time to the days when young callants clashed with marauding bands of English raiders in a thousand and one skirmishes which helped to mould the independent spirit of their inhabitants.

Perhaps the most stirring and colourful of them all is the Selkirk Common Riding each June when a cavalcade of more than five hundred steeds ride the Burgh Marches and the Standard Bearer commemorates the fallen of the bloody Flodden battlefield - and the town's solitary survivor who returned to a hero's welcome.

There is nothing quite like the feeling of being wakened by the burgh's bands as they parade the streets while most Souters (Selkirk folk) are still asleep, urging them to march with them and sing the rousing chorus, "Hail! Smiling Morn" to coax the sun to rise and show its face.

Fierce rivalry among the Border towns which stage their own weekend festivals through these months is itself a way of life. One proud resident is once said to have boasted that "a day out of Hawick was a day wasted". At each gathering, you will hear locals, and exiles who have returned from foreign parts to sing along, join in old refrains which tell of daring deeds long ago, and how their "toon" stands head and shoulders above "a' ithers".

Grown men have been known to shed a tear, such is the depth of the emotional charge at some sessions. And don't believe the sceptics who dare to suggest that the traditional early morning draught - a tot of black rum and milk to put a lining on the stomach for the big day ahead - could provide a possible alternative explanation.

If these wonderful annual get-togethers were all Border counties had to lure outsiders in, they would of course, be reason enough. But all year round, you will find the towns and villages have much more to offer, not least the people themselves, who are genuine and generous hosts.

The main nucleus of the antiques and fine art trade is sprinkled throughout Roxburghshire, Selkirkshire and Berwickshire on the central/eastern side of the country, while further west, antiques and other attractions are to be found around the Kirkcudbright area.

Visitors flock in their thousands to Kelso and Jedburgh, each with an abbey and a quaint old-world charm which still survives today, while Hawick's Wilton Lodge Park and its museum will reveal some of the

secrets on just what makes a Teri (Hawick person) tick. There are good quality antiques shops to be found in all three towns (a hugh stock to view in Jedburgh) and one of the best privately run art galleries is located in the hamlet of Ancrum.

Half an hour to the west of Hawick, nestling in the Liddesdale valley, lies the village of Newcastleton where you are guaranteed to encounter a cheery face, fine hospitality and if you wish, peaceful tranquility on the moors and hills which envelop Copshawholm.

The popular destination for a Sunday drive has a single antiques shop which also doubles as a coffee shop and restaurant - and where the owner and her staff will leave you contentedly smiling like a Cheshire cat after sampling the home baking.

Visitors who are quick enough off their mark may be able to snap up a locally-baked Barley Fadge (any day but Sunday) before they all disappear like snow off a dyke from the shelves of the nearby baker's shop. And those planning a riverside barbecue should make for Elliot's the butchers where the Cumberland sausages would win gold medals in any banger contest.

Another popular Sunday haunt for those who like a satisfying rummage is the village of Greenlaw in Berwickshire where a massive former town hall on the village green is stuffed with everything from linen, second-hand gardening tools and bric-a-brac to pictures and furniture. The family-run business also caters for the antiques trade with a mainstream mix of quality furniture and smaller items, from different premises.

As usual, it is always worth checking the public notice pages in local newspapers for auction sales, antiques fairs, charity and car boot sales which take place at regular intervals throughout the year.

1 ANCRUM GALLERY

Ancrum, near Jedburgh (A68),
Roxburghshire TD8 1RD.
Tel: 08353 340. Eve. also.
Proprietrix: Dr. Moira Simmons and
Mrs. Sheena Lawrie.
Changing exhibitions of leading
contemporary artists. We have an
excellent stock of 20th century
paintings.
Open six days 12-5pm. Closed Tues.

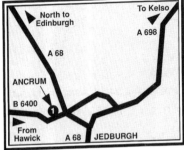

2 CHAPEL ANTIQUES

Chapel Farm, Kirkcudbright DG6 4NG.
Tel: 055 722 281. Eve. also.
Proprietrix: Alison Bradley.
Huge stock of ceramics, metalware,
period and shipping furniture. Browsers
paradise at Chapel Farm. Houses
cleared.
Open: 2-4pm or on chance at any other
time.

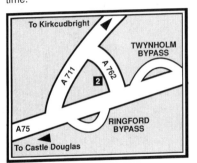

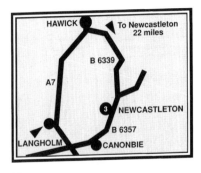

3 JANE ELLIOT ANTIQUES

Copshaw Kitchen Restaurant, 4 North
Hermitage Street, Newcastleton,
Roxburghshire TD9 ORB.
Tel: 03873 75250. Eve: 03873 75233.
An Aladdin's cave of linen and
ceramics, specialising in jug and bowl
sets and decorative arts.
Open: 10am-6pm daily, except Tues.
Also evenings Wed-Sat.

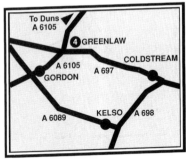

4 GREENLAW ANTIQUES

Eildon View, Duns Road, Greenlaw,
Berwickshire TD10 6XJ.
Tel: 03616 220.
Proprietors: Mr. & Mrs. A. Brotherstone.
Vast and varied stock of antiques in
former town hall and two warehouses.
Sun: 12.30-5pm. Wed: 10.30am-5pm
Also by appointment.

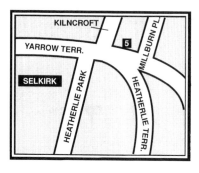

5 HEATHERLIE ANTIQUES
6/8 Heatherlie Terrace, Selkirk
TD7 5AH. Tel: 0750 20114.
Proprietor: Douglas Scott.
General antiques. Easy parking.
Open: 9.30am-5pm.
Closed for lunch:12.30-2pm.

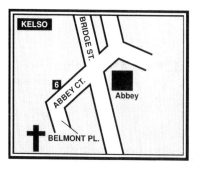

6 HONOR HORNE SMALL ANTIQUES
3a Abbey Court, Kelso, Roxburghshire
TD5 7JA.
Tel: 0573 224805. Eve: 0573 225518.
Interesting and decorative period china,
glass, Scottish pottery and small,
portable pieces of furniture.
Open: 10am-12.30pm; 2.30-5pm.
Closed Wednesday.

7 JAMES INGLES
57 High Street, Hawick, Roxburgh
TD9 9BP. Tel: 0450 72574.
The leading jewellers, where old
fashioned service is uppermost.
Mon-Fri: 9am-5.30pm. Sat: 9am-5pm.
Tuesday: early closing.

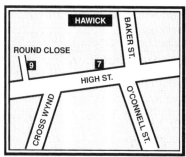

8 R. & M. TURNER (ANTIQUES) LTD
34-36 High Street, Jedburgh TD8 6AG.
Tel: 0835 863445.
Visit the largest antique shop in the
borders. Large interesting varied stock,
including interior design.
Mon-Sat: 9.30am-5.30pm.

9 RUTH WALKER RESTORATIONS
4 Round Close, Hawick TD9 9DF.
General restoration workshop, furniture,
ceramics, frames. Small stock of
ceramics, antique/second-hand furniture
and bric-a-brac.
Mon-Fri: 9am-5pm, unless on call.

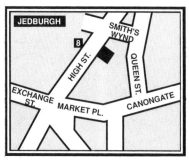

A TALE OF TWO TOWNS

THE GEORGIAN HOUSE	GLADSTONE'S LAND
In the elegant New Town is No 7 Charlotte Square, Edinburgh, where you can absorb the splendid atmosphere of the Georgian era.	This 17th-century merchant's house is in the Lawnmarket, near the castle. Restored and furnished, it is typical of the Old Town of Edinburgh.

Both houses are open to visitors.
Open: Monday-Saturday 10-5
Sundays 2-5
(last admission half-hour before closing time)

CHARLOTTE Square, Edinburgh... A Masterpiece of Urban Architecture by Robert Adam.
Photo: Scottish Tourist Board.

ollectors, imagine a fabulously vast market where the treasures of the world are tantalisingly spread out before you. All the richness and colour and variety of far-flung climes and their exotic merchandise has passed this way for centuries; some ancient artefacts whose beauty will for ever delight the eye and heart, the remainder a great pot pourri of precious raw materials awaiting transformation at the hands of master craftsmen. Rare woods and veneers from the Americas and Far East; exotic fruit woods for inlay and marquetry; precious metals and stones to be fashioned at the benches of gold and silversmiths...

Imagine, too, that market supported by a booming trade in the homespun crafts and manufacturing processes of the day - clock making, pottery, glass, guns and armour ... Then move forward in time to today and call it Edinburgh.

That is the reality of Scotland's capital city. It is a veritable storehouse of treasures, often cropping up in the most unexpected places, and we will lead you to them, whether they lie in the city's multifarious museums and art institutions, public and private galleries, or in the antique warehouses, High Street shops, bric-a-brac basements and curio corners.

That's one of the delights of Edinburgh; it has a knack of constantly surprising you.

London apart, no other city in the United Kingdom offers such a rich diversity of trading activity.

The sheer breadth of its goods and services impress even the most seasoned dealers who make regular forays into its environs.

The market place here covers a vast spectrum of interst to the trade and private buyer, and while we can't encapsulate it all in this chapter (for the complete range see our extensive index), we most certainly can give a hint of the flavour.

In the mainstream antique shops - the bulk of them are to be found in the city centre on either side of Princes Street - the huge range includes: Period, Victorian and Edwardian furniture, stripped pine and country items, porcelain, glass and ceramics, Art Nouveau and deco, clocks and barometers, oriental rugs and carpets, antique jewellery, decorative objects, interior design articles, silverware and plate, fire surrounds and inserts, and curios and bric-a-brac galore.

For the collectors there is a marvellous assortment of specialities ranging from ethnic art, old toys, teddies and dolls, radios and telephones, wind-up gramophones, scientific and nautical instruments, collectors' records, antiquarian books and Scottish silver to linen and lace, period costume and accessories, textiles, shawls and quilts, samplers, vintage watches, hand-decorated pottery, stamps, coins, medals, militaria, postcards and cigarette cards.

The list goes on: Chair specialists and dealerships carrying architectural metalwork, antique brass furnishings and fittings, Scottish antiquities and, of course, Fine Art.

Edinburgh is a recognised European art centre, acknowledged as having the largest number of exhibition venues per head of population anywhere in Britain, and the top firms from the the auction world are well represented. Dozens of galleries make it impressive by any standards. All the important

names of Scottish art can be found in this noble spread, and one of the most pleasing aspects about these galleries is that, as well as having on show the great oil paintings, watercolours and prints, many also diversify. They are not averse to showing off the talents of a new breed of contemporary artists, a trend which has attracted a completely fresh generation of buyers.

In the public sector, the stature of the city's municipal collection is immense, and the National Gallery of Scotland are custodians of a remarkable collection of more than a thousand important works by virtually all of the old Masters. Their purchasing policy has ensured that, over the past 160 years, the collection has grown from strength to strength and many major works have recently been acquired.

The National Gallery of Modern Art is to be found in the former John Watson's School, a splendid country-style property in well tended grounds which feature larger sculptures, including pieces by Henry Moore. Inside its spacious rooms, paintings and objects from the hands of Picasso, Braque, Miro, Magritte, Ernst and Lichtenstein are to be admired. The collection records the development of painting over the last century and a fine selection of recent Scottish works has been added and is constantly being expanded.

The initials, RSA, have graced many an important canvas over the years, being the illustrious hallmark of members of the Royal Scottish Academy, and inside this imposing institution (beside the National Gallery of Scotland in The Mound, just off Princes Street) the work of academicians and invited artists can be enjoyed.

The RSA roll call of honour is extensive, to say the least. Any Scottish artist of note, right up to the present day, is to be found therein. In the endless list you will come across such eminent figures as Sir Noel Paton, Sir Henry Raeburn, Sir David Wilkie, James Guthrie, Robert Gemmell Hutchinson and Mary Armour.

Those with a love of antiquities but who wish to look and learn, not buy, buy, buy, will find a city bristling with museums and fascinating attractions, and while Edinburgh's famous castle will always continue to draw the crowds and reigns supreme as the counrty's top visitor attraction, a multitude of other important venues deserve inspection.

The list is massive and would fill a book in itself, such is the rich and regal past of this truly royal city. Of course, we have our favourites - among them the splendid Georgian House in pristine Charlotte Square; Huntly House Museum, the enchanting Museum of Childhood, the National Museum of Antiquities in Queen Street and the Royal Scottish Museum in Chamber Street. In each of these can be seen the artistry and craftsmanship of true masters whose works remain an enduring testament to their lives.

Whytock and Reid mahogony side table (c. 1910) which sold for £2,800 in auction.   Photo: William Hardie Ltd.

It is heartening to report that in today's age of mass production and the throw-away society, the demand for those traditional skills remains - fostered by the gifted work of cabinetmakers, wood carvers, specialist restorers and others. It takes courage to eschew the dictates of fashion and factory for the long hours involved in creating the single one-off, hand-made item. In the '50s, the boom years of the cheap and nasty, there was a real danger that those skills would disappear, starved out of existance by the clamour of consumerism.

But, in the Edinburgh of the 1990s, things have come full circle and fat order books are now commonplace. That healthy revival is due in no small measure to the exceedingly high level of workmanship available.

While sizeable concentrations of antique shops and galleries exist in such areas as George Street, Dundas Street, Thistle Street, St Stephen Street and the many thoroughfares around this area to the North of Princes Street; and in the Victoria Street, Grassmarket, West Crosscauseway, Causewayside and Bruntsfield areas to the South, the visitor should not neglect other parts of the city.

Dotted around Edinburgh's central and outlying areas, and at its extremities, are many rewarding shops awaiting discovery. One of the richest of these seams is in Leith where the core of the antiques scene is a thriving trade in shipping goods, furniture and general goods.

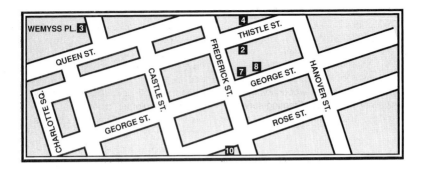

1 LAURANCE BLACK LIMITED
45 Cumberland Street, Edinburgh
EH3 6RA.
Tel: 031 557 4545.
Proprietors: L. Black and S.J. Campbell.
Scottish antiques, 18th & 19th century
furniture, treen, metalwork, pottery,
porcelain, glass and works of art.
Mon-Fri: 10am-5pm; Sat: 10am-1pm.

2 JOSEPH H. BONNAR
72 Thistle Street, Edinburgh EH2 1EN.
Tel: 031 226 2811.
The best collection of antique jewellery
seen anywhere, most reasonably priced
for such high quality - The London
Times.
Mon-Sat: 10.30am-5pm. Or by
appointment.

3 CHRISTIE'S
5 Wemyss Place, Edinburgh EH3 6DH.
Tel: 031 225 4756. Fax: 031 225 1723.
Valuations for insurance and tax
purposes. Free advice on buying and
selling through Christie's international
auction rooms.
Mon-Fri: 9am-5pm.

4 ELLEN FORD ANTIQUES
37 Thistle Street, Edinburgh EH1 2DY.
Tel: 031 225 6350. Eve: 031 552 3412.
Decorative items, paintings, prints,
china, furniture.
Open: Flexible. When closed phone
031-552-3412.

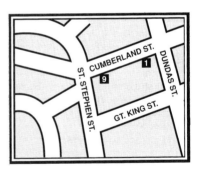

5 GLADRAGS
17 Henderson Row, Edinburgh.
Tel: 031 557 1916.
Proprietrix: Kate Cameron.
Unique selection of exquisite period
clothes. Accessories & costume
jewellery. Lace-edged table/bed linen &
Paisley shawls. Established 1977.
Tues-Sat: 10.30am-6pm.

6 HANOVER FINE ARTS

22a Dundas Street, Edinburgh EH3 6JN
Tel: 031 556 2181.
Proprietor: Richard Ireland.
Regular exhibitions (15 p.a.) of
contemporary Scottish paintings,
ceramics, sculpture, woodcarvings,
jewellery and prints. Framing service.
Mon-Fri: 10.30am-6pm. Sat: 10am-4pm.

7 MALCOLM INNES GALLERY

67 George Street, Edinburgh EH2 2JG.
Tel: 031 226 4151.
Proprietor: Anthony Woodd.
Scottish landscape, sporting and
military pictures. Natural history
sculptures.
Mon-Fri: 9.30am-6pm. Sat: 10am-1pm.

8 LYON & TURNBULL LTD

51 George Street, Edinburgh EH2 2HT.
Tel: 031 225 4627/8.
Proprietors: Ord K. Reid K.St.J., J.P.;
Wm. A. Plews, F.G.A., F.S.V.A.(Secy.);
A.G. Whyte, F.G.A., F.S.V.A.;
R.McVicar.
Edinburgh's oldest auctioneers, founded
1826. Daily sales include antique
furniture, china, pictures, silver plate,
jewellery etc.
Mon-Fri: 9am-5pm; Sat: 9am-1pm.

9 OPEN EYE GALLERY

75/79 Cumberland Street, Edinburgh
EH3 6RD.
Tel: 031 557 1020.
Proprietors: Thomas and Pamela
Wilson.
Changing exhibitions of contemporary
paintings, sculpture, ceramics and
jewellery. Early 20th century etchings
and studio ceramics.
Mon-Fri: 10am-6pm. Sat: 10am-4pm.

10 JOHN WHYTE, Licensed Broker

116 Rose Street, Edinburgh EH2 3JF.
Tel: 031 225 2140.
Antique clocks, rings, jewellery, silver
etc.; old gold and silver bought for cash.
Mon-Fri: 9.30am-5.15pm.
Sat: 9.30am-12.15pm.

5 WILD ROSE ANTIQUES

15 Henderson Row, Edinburgh.
Tel: 031 557 1916.
Proprietors: E. & Kate Cameron.
Distinctive specialist shop presenting
select decorative/funtional silver; ladies/
gents jewellery; porcelain, pottery, glass
& metalware. Established 1975.
Tues-Sat: 10.30am-6pm.

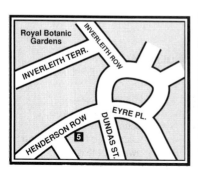

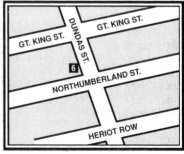

1 KENNETH W. BRUCE

41 St. Stephen Street, Edinburgh
EH3 5AH.
Tel: 031 226 5984. Eve: 031 669 6673.
Jewellery, silver, curios, coins, postal
history. Highest prices paid for scrap
gold and silver. Mon-Sat: 10am-4.30pm.

2 CHIT-CHAT ANTIQUES

134 St. Stephen Street, Edinburgh
EH3 5AA. Tel: 031 225 9660.
Proprietrix: Victoria Reid.
Large selection of antique and second-
hand cutlery, linen and lace; also
ceramics, glass, silver plate etc.
Wed-Sat: 11am-5pm.

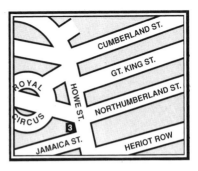

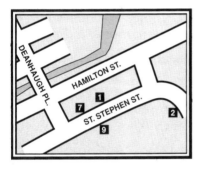

3 FORREST McKAY

38 Howe Street, Edinburgh EH3 6TH.
Tel: 031 226 2589.
Partners: M.A. Forrest and S.M. McKay.
Specialists in Scottish School paintings
from 18th to 20th century. Decorative
arts, framing and restoration.
Mon-Fri: 10am-6pm. Sat: 10am-1pm.

4 GALERIE MIRAGES

46a Raeburn Place, Edinburgh EH4 1HL.
Proprietrix: Sheila Dhariwai.
Ethnic art, antique furniture, wood
carvings, silver jewellery, textiles, tribal
artefacts from India, Central Asia.
Tue-Fri:10.30am-4.30pm.Sat:10am-5pm.

5 HAND IN HAND

3 North West Circus Place,
Edinburgh EH3 6ST. Tel: 031 226 3598.
Proprietrix: Mrs. Ruth Hand.
Victorian/Edwardian soft furnishings,
Paisley shawls, quilts, linens and lace;
period costumes, jewellery and
accessories.
Tues-Sat: 10am-5.30pm. Closed Mon.

6 THE KIMONO COMPANY

5 Carlton Street, Edinburgh, EH4 1NE.
Tel: 031 332 1519. Eve. also.
Proprietors: Joanne Soroka and Mike
Griffiths.
Antique, wearable Japanese clothing at
affordable prices - kimonos, haori
(jackets), happi coats - mainly silk, all
hand-made.
By appointment only.

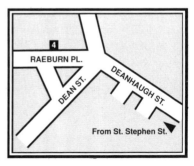

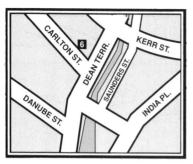

2 REID & REID LTD.

134 St. Stephen Street, Edinburgh
EH3 5AA.
Tel: 031 225 9660.
Proprietor: William Reid.
Antiquarian/second-hand books
(literature, topography, sports, travel,
art, illustrated etc), etchings, engravings
and lithographs.
Wed-Sat: 11am-5pm.

9 36 ST. STEPHEN STREET

36 St. Stephen Street, Edinburgh.
Proprietor: G.H. White.
Cutlery; 19th century drinking glasses;
kitchenalia; antique and 20th century
china, glass, ceramics and curios; Art
Nouveau/Deco.
Mon-Sat: 11am-5.30pm.

7 MONTRESOR

35 St. Stephen Street, Edinburgh
EH3 5AH.
Tel: 031 220 6877.
Genuine antique and designer costume
jewellery and accessories; lighting
specialists, Art Nouveau and Art Deco.
Tues-Sat: 10.30am-1pm; 2-6pm.

8 QUADRANT ANTIQUES

5 North West Circus Place,
Edinburgh EH3.
Tel: 031 226 7282.
Nautical items, scientific instruments,
furniture, clocks, pictures, old pub
mirrors, barometers, dolls, stained
glass, militaria.
Mon-Sat: 10am-5.30pm. Or by
appointment.

10 WHYTOCK & REID

Sunbury House, Belford Mews,
Edinburgh EH4 3DN.
Tel: 031 226 4911.
Proprietors: David C. & J. C. Reid.
18th & 19th century furniture, oriental
rugs and carpets, restoration of
furniture. Cabinetmakers, upholsterers
and polishers.
Mon-Fri: 9am-5.30pm.
Sat: 9am-12.30pm.

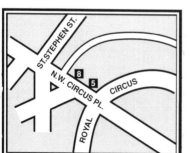

1 BEAVER GLASS RESTORATION

23 Hatton Place, Edinburgh EH9 1UB.
Tel: 031 667 8996.
Proprietor: P.D. Beaver.
Specialists in economical restoration of chipped or cloudy glassware, domestic, decorative or collectable. Stoppers available.
Mon-Fri: 9am-5pm.

2 BUCCLEUCH ANTIQUES

90 Buccleuch Street, Edinburgh EH8 9NH.
Tel: 031 667 7414. Eve: 031 552 1712.
Proprietrix: Susanna Harrison.
Victorian and Edwardian furniture, paintings, old picture frames, antiquarian books, china and glass.
Mon-Sat: 11am-5pm.

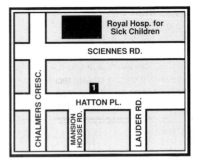

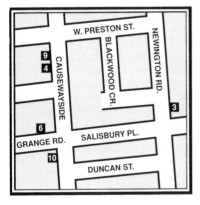

3 CASEY'S VINTAGE CAMERAS

63 Newington Road, Edinburgh EH9 1QW.
Tel: 031 667 8515.
Proprietor: James Casey.
All old vintage cameras from 1850's to 1970's, vintage projectors, cine cameras and anything photographic.
Please telephone to arrange appointment.

4 THE CHAIRWOMAN

33/45 Causewayside, Edinburgh EH9 1QF.
Tel: 031 668 4136.
Proprietrix: Patricia Grubb.
Specialists in traditional upholstery. Large selection of sofas, chairs, Chesterfields etc. for sale.
Mon-Fri: 8.30am-5pm. Sat:10am-6pm.

5 DAVIDSON AND BEGG ANTIQUES LTD

183/189 Causewayside, Edinburgh EH9 1PH.
Tel: 031 662 4221.
Proprietor: Mr. Eric Davidson & Mr. Robert Begg.
Magnificent selection of Georgian and Victorian English furniture as well as clocks, bronzes and decorative items.
Mon-Sat: 9am-5.30pm.

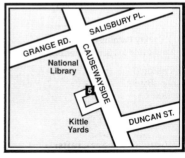

6 THE NEST EGG

5 Grange Road, Edinburgh EH9 1UH.
Tel: 031 667 2328. Eve: 031 667 8996.
Proprietors: Phil A. Beaver and Hugo.
Antiques, classic radios and telephones.
Edinburgh's unique classic technology
shop. Phones and radios repaired and
restored. Mon-Sat: 10am-6pm.

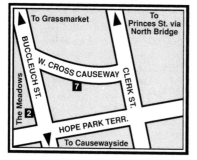

7 NOW AND THEN

7 & 9 West Crosscauseway,
Edinburgh EH8 9JW.
Tel: 031 668 2927. Eve: 031 226 2867.
Proprietor: David Gordon.
Old telephones and radios (with
guarantees), pre-war tin trains, cars,
Dinky toys, advertising and automobilia.
Mon-Fri: 11am-6pm. Sat:10am-6pm.

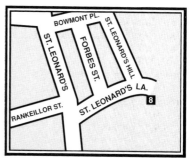

8 OUT OF THE NOMAD'S TENT

21 St. Leonard's Lane, Edinburgh
EH8 9SH. Tel: 031 662 1612.
Proprietor: Rufus Reade.
Tribal rugs, jewellery, textiles collected
at source from Western and Central
Asia. Trade and export welcome.
Tues-Sat: 10am-5pm.

9 UPSTAIRS, DOWNSTAIRS

21a Causewayside,Edinburgh EH9 1QF.
Tel: 031 668 4136.
Proprietrix: Patricia Grubb.
Decorative antiques, good quality
furniture, small general antiques and
collectors' items. Specialists in
upholstered chairs.
Mon-Fri: 11am-5pm. Sat: 10am-6pm.

10 VICTORIA WRIGHT ANTIQUES

51 Causewayside, Edinburgh EH9 1QF.
Furniture, ceramics, glass, curiosities
and a large variety of small items.
Articles bought and sold.
Mon-Sat: 11am-4.30pm. Closed Thurs.

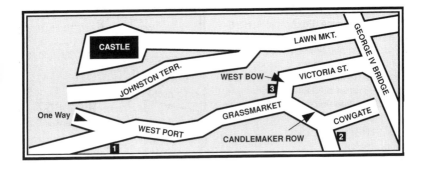

1 ANOTHER TIME - ANOTHER PLACE
9 Eastfountainbridge, Edinburgh
EH3 9BH.
Tel: 031 669 3082. Eve. also.
Proprietrix: Mrs A. Averbuch.
Period clothing and accessories;
costume jewellery, soft furnishings and
textiles, linen and lace. We buy and sell.
Mon-Sat: 1-5pm.

2 ANOTHER WORLD
25 Candlemaker Row, Edinburgh
EH1 2QG.
Tel: 031 225 1988.
Proprietrix: Dorothy Harrison.
Old netsuke, sword fittings, oriental art.
Appointments welcome.
Wed, Fri, Sat: 1pm-5pm.

3 BOW WELL ANTIQUES
103 West Bow, Edinburgh EH1 2JP.
Tel: 031 225 3335.
Proprietors: M.E. Bennett-Levy, Murdo
McLeod, George Haggarty.
Scottish jewellery, regalia, pottery,
clocks, silver, silver-plate,
gramophones, scientific instruments,
light fittings, furniture.
Open: 10am-6pm.

4 D. L. CAVANAGH (ANTIQUES)
49 Cockburn Street, Edinburgh
EH1 1BS.
Tel: 031 226 3391.
World coins, medals, militaria, gold and
silver jewellery, silver and plate,
antiques and curios, postcards.
Mon-Sat: 11am-5pm.

5 TRIST AND McBAIN
9 Canongate Venture, New Street,
Edinburgh EH8 8BH. Tel: 031 557 3828.
Proprietors: William Trist & Andrew
McBain.
Quality cabinetmaking, cane and rush
seating, wood turning, leathers, French
polishing, chair making, upholstery and
antique furniture restoration.
Mon-Fri: 8.30am-5.30pm.
Sat: by appointment.

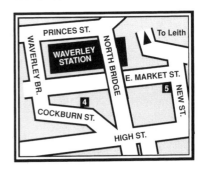

6 ARCHWAY ANTIQUES

3 Comiston Place, Edinburgh, EH10 6AF.
Tel: 031 669 4568. Eve. only.
Proprietors: Mrs. Patricia E. and
Mr. Michael Davidson.
Selection of china, glass, linen, Scottish
pottery and small furniture.
Mon-Fri:12noon-5.pm.Sat:11am-5.30pm.

7 CRAIGLEA CLOCKS

88 Comiston Rd, Edinburgh EH10 5JQ
Tel: 031 452 8568. Eve: 031 447 6334.
Antique clocks, barometers and small
furniture bought, sold and repaired.
Mon-Sat: 10am-1pm; 2-5.30pm. Closed
all day Wed.

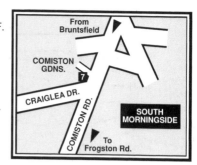

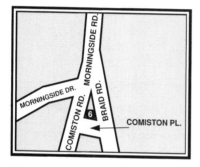

8 E. B. FORREST & CO. ANTIQUES

3 Barclay Terrace, Edinburgh
EH10 4HP. Tel: 031 229 3156.
Interesting jewellery, glass, china and
objets d'art; silver/plate. We buy and
sell. Trade welcome.
Mon-Sat: 10.30am-5pm.

9 KAIMES SMITHY ANTIQUES

Kaimes Junction, 79 Howdenhall Road,
Edinburgh. Proprietor: J. Lynch
Tel: 031 441 2076. Eve. also.
Wide selection of good quality 18-20th
century furniture, clocks, bric-a-brac.
(Quality furniture always wanted).
Tues, Wed, Fri, Sat: 1.30pm-5.30pm.
Or by appointment. TRADE WELCOME.

10 YOUNG ANTIQUES

36 Bruntsfield Place, Edinburgh
EH10 4HJ. Tel: 031 229 1361.
Proprietor: T.C. Young.
British & Oriental porcelain, glass,
paintings, antique Victorian and
Edwardian furniture, Persian rugs, Art
Nouveau and Art Deco.
Mon-Sat: 10.30am-1.30pm; 2-5.30pm.
Closed Wednesday afternoon.

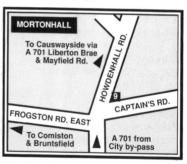

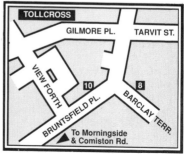

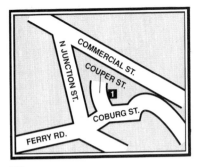

1 E.A.S.Y.

Edinburgh & Glasgow Architectural
Salvage Yards, Unit 6, Couper Street,
Edinburgh EH6 6HH.Tel: 031 554 7077.
Also at: 85-87 Colvend Street, Glasgow
G40 4DU. Tel: 041 556 7772.
Partners: Neil & Elizabeth Barrass.
Original fixtures and fittings, panel doors,
shutters, mouldings, baths, sinks,
radiators, fireplaces, bought and sold.
Mon-Fri: 9am-5pm. Sat: 12 noon-5pm.

2 GEORGIAN ANTIQUES

10 Pattison Street, Leith Links,
Edinburgh EH6 7HF.
Tel: 031 553 7286 (24 hrs).
Fax: 031 558 6299.
Proprietors: Dr. P. Dixon, Mr J. Dixon.
Largest stock (50,000 sq. ft.) of
Edwardian, Victorian, Georgian and
shipping furniture,& smalls, in Britain.
Mon-Fri: 8.30am-5.30pm.Sat: 10am-1pm.

3 T. & J. W. NEILSON LTD.

192 Morrison Street, Edinburgh
EH3 8EB.
Tel: 031 229 5591.
Wide selection of quality wood/marble
chimney pieces, interiors, dog grates,
hobs, fenders, fireside accessories.
Mon-Fri: 9am-1pm; 2-5pm. Sat: 9-1pm.

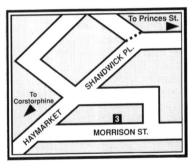

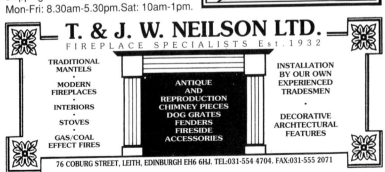

Leith From The Pier, drawn by A.S. Masson & engraved by John Gellatly (c.1800). Photo: Edinburgh Central Library

4 THE THURSDAY SHOP

5 Clermiston Road, Corstorphine,
Edinburgh.
Tel: 031 334 3696.
Proprietrix: Jean Robertson.
Interesting selection of china, paintings,
jewellery, linen and good quality bric-a-
brac bought and sold.
Mon-Sat: 10.30am-5pm. Closed Wed.

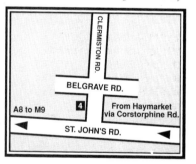

29

Paisley Museum & Art Galleries

This late 19th century Museum & Art Gallery houses the
world famous collection of Paisley shawls. Displays trace
the history of the Paisley Pattern; the development of
weaving techniques is explained and the social aspects of
what was a tight knit weaving community are explored.

There are also fine collections of local history, natural
history, ceramics and Scottish paintings.

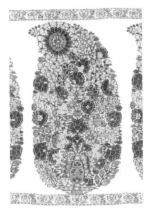

Paisley Shawls

One of the 19th century's most
enduring fashions was for the
Paisley shawl. Indian shawls
were imported and copied in
various European centres but
nowhere more successfully
than in Paisley. The town's
Museum preserves the world's
largest collection of the exoti-
cally patterned garments along
with original design books and
weaving equipment.

Paisley Museum & Art Galleries,
High Street, Paisley, PA1 2BA, Telephone: 041-889 3151/2/3
Opening hours: Mon - Sat, 10am-5pm, Closed Sunday

Department of Arts & Libraries
Renfrew District Council

astles and Queens, battlefields and clifftops, conservation villages and coal mines, fine craftsmen, museums, galleries, antiques and book shops...that's all in store on this fabulous East Lothian trip.

It's a full day's outing, but don't take the golf clubs or you'll never get far! East Lothian boasts 16 golf courses, including the world-famous Muirfield links at Gullane. Founded in 1744, this magnificent course has witnessed the drama of many a British Open Championship final.

East Lothian, with conservation villages and leafy byways aplenty, is an eclectic mix of fine buildings, past industrial glories and richness of character. It is a blend of coast and country, town and mining village - and we have plotted this outing to reflect that diversity.

The "Honest Toun" of Musselburgh is a race course town which still has a raffish seaside charm about it. Its importance in Scottish history, however, goes back a lot further than its connections with the Sport of Kings. The town is sited on the main Eastern route between Scotland and England and at great moments in the affairs of state, many military cavalcades have tramped across the ancient bridge which spans the River Esk at that point. The Roman bridge is one of the country's most historic structures, and down the centuries has echoed to the sound of marching soldiers...Edward II's vanquished army, Cromwell's Cavalry and Mary Queen of Scots, herself, have all traversed its ancient span for appointments with their respective destinies.

Musselburgh town centre, with many architectural gems, gives pride of place to the Dutch-style Tolbooth, built in 1590, and not far from that notable landmark is our first stop.

East of Musselburgh, along the coast, is Preston Grange, where the age of steam is still celebrated in an interesting visitors' centre which incorporates the Scottish Mining Museum. During the summer, on the first Sunday of every month,steam enthusiasts flock to see the former colliery locomotives in action. Another big attraction at the site is the great Cornish steam engine which for more than 80 years pumped water from the mine.

Linking up with the Al, we arrive, in 15 minutes or so, at one of the finest 18th century towns in Britain - gracious Haddington.

With its unspoilt architecture, pleasing street frontages and courtyards and lanes, there is almost a country tranquility about its thoroughfares.

The Town House, Haddington , designed in 1748 by William Adam. Photo: East Lothian District Council

Preston MIll, East Linton. Scotland's only working meal mill. Photo: East Lothian District Council

Its focal point is the Town House, an imposing spire-topped building created in 1748 by William Adam, the father of the famous Robert. It occupies a dominant position in an irregular triangle of streets which encompass two antique shops.

Leaving Haddington by the A6137, we make for Gullane. Halfway there, is a worthwhile halt for enthusiasts of vintage and veteran cars and automobilia. The Myreton Motor Museum contains a fascinating collection of vehicles, motor cycles, vans and bicycles from 1897 onwards.

Five miles around the coast, as we head for Dunbar, North Berwick throws up two spectacular landmarks. Perched high upon a sheer clifftop are the imposing ruins of 14th century Tantallon Castle, and out to sea, the giant stone column of the bass Rock, rising steep and black 350 ft. above the crashing waves of the North Sea.

After you have gathered your breath, enjoy a 15-minute drive around the rugged coastline and you arrive at Dunbar, the birthplace of John Muir, a Victorian conservationist who has a glacier in Alaska named after him and was responsible for the foundation of two of the USA's most famous national parks - Yosemite and Sequoia. The town has its own lasting monument to the achievements of the man in the very fitting form of a large country park, a mile-long retreat containing Dunbar Castle.

Back along the Al, we reach East Linton, a former 18th century mill village rich in character and things to see. Situated in the old Station House is the first of our local specialists. As so often is the case in areas where the tradition of the Big House pertains, skills and crafts once needed to service the elegance of that lifestyle, remain. At Crauchie, on the outskirts of the village, are the workshops and considerable talents of Anselm Fraser, one of the most noted craftsmen in Scotland. He has handled many a major commission in painstaking restoration work, and some of the area's country houses are graced by examples of his fine, hand-crafted furniture.

To the North of East Linton is Traprain Law - the core of an extinct volcano - which for 16 centuries held a secret undreamed of by the local people. In 1919, on its slopes, was unearthed a rare hoard of fourth century silver - one of the most romantic finds which fires the imagination of collectors everywhere. The artefacts brought to light in this important discovery are now on display in the National Museum of Antiquities in Edinburgh.

Just outside the village, incidently, is a beautifully restored working water mill owned by the National Trust for Scotland.

Our route back to Edinburgh follows a trail through more charming East Lothian villages, with two of them, Gifford and Pencaitland, being quite outstanding. Gifford, some seven miles from Stenton on the B6370, is the birthplace of John Witherspoon, one of the signatories of the American Declaration of Independence. The village itself, is set against a most spectacular backdrop as the woods of Yester sweep right down to the end of the main street. Making for Tranent, we reach the 17th century village of Pencaitland where a remarkably fine example of a church dating back 800 years is the most noteworthy building. It and its quaint, old-world graveyard are well worth exploring. Near Tranent, too, is the tiny village of Macmerry which gave its name to the Mak' Merry hand-painted pottery first produced in 1919 and now highly prized by a growing number of collectors.

1 FINE DESIGN (OLD & NEW)

6 Court Street, Haddington,
East Lothian EH41 4QZ.
Tel: 062 082 4838. Eve. 062 082 6168.
Proprietors: Melanie & Douglas Nicoll.
Varied selection of antique jewellery,
pottery, porcelain, silver, silver plate,
small furniture and decorative items.
Mon-Sat: 10am-12.45; 2.15-5.30pm.
Jan, Feb. March: Closed Thursdays
(otherwise half day).

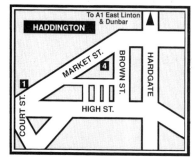

2 ANSELM FRASER

The Carthouse, Crauchie, East Linton,
East Lothian EH40. Tel: 0620 860067.
Fine quality furniture restoration by
professional craftsmen. Faithful copies
made to order. Courses also offered.
9am-4.30pm (tel. appointments only).

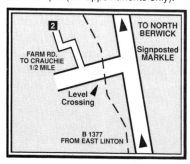

3 GULLANE ANTIQUES

5 Rosebery Place, Gullane,
East Lothian. Tel: 0620 842326. (Eve.)
Proprietor: E. A. Lindsay.
Large general stock including glass,
ceramics, jewellery, and collectables -
mainly 19th and early 20th century.
Mon, Tues, Fri, Sat: 10.30am-1pm;
2.30-5pm.Thurs: 2.30-5pm.Closed Wed.

4 LESLIE & LESLIE

77 Market Street, Haddington EH41 3JJ.
Tel: 062 082 2241. Eve: 062 082 3262.
Proprietor: R. Skea.
General antiques and reproduction
furniture; quarterly antique auctions;
removals and storage. Mon-Fri:9am-5pm.

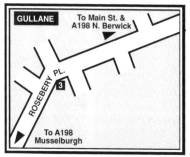

An unusual small Mak' Merry pot with painted lid.
Photo: Fergus & Rose Hall

An extremely rare Mak' Merry slop pail. Photo: Fergus & Rose Hall.

1 LATTO BOOKS

Goosegreen Gallery, 3 Eskside East,
Musselburgh, Midlothian EH21 7RU.
Tel: 031 665 2651.
Eve: Port Seton 810601.
Proprietor: Adam C. A. Latto.
General stock; speciality subjects,
Scottish, Edinburgh, golf and jazz.
Catalogues issued free.
Mon-Sat: 9am-5pm. Half day Wed.

2 LINTON COUNTRY FURNITURE

Station House, East Linton, EH40 3DP.
Tel: 0620 860068.
Proprietors: J.D. Spence &
Mrs. J. Spence.
Antique and reproduction pine
showroom. Stripping service, pine
furniture made to measure.
Mon-Sat: 8am-5pm. Sun: 1-5pm.

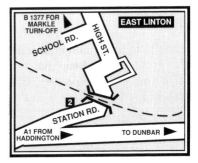

ur abiding memory of Fife isn't its varied scenery, its ruggedly beautiful coastline with trim fishing villages clinging against it, or even its deeply historic past. It is the friendliness of its people.

In Fife - the Kingdom over the Forth Bridge from Edinburgh - a little soft laughter and a ready smile make the world go round. There is an openness and natural courtesy about Fife folk which fairly lifts the spirit. It is one of the reasons we love going there: They have the knack of making strangers feel completely at home - a rare gift indeed in these hustle, bustle times.

With the area's traditional links with pottery production, it is not surprising to find a proliferation of Wemyss Ware and lesser known, but rapidly appreciating, Bough hand-decorated pots and plates. In Kirkcaldy, where you would expect to find a substantial presence, the town's municipal museum and art gallery contains a remarkable collection of locally produced pottery.

In general the standard of trading activity throughout Fife falls in the medium to quality range of antiques, with a nice spread of general bric-a-brac shops and glory-holes to keep bargain hunters happy.

A Wemyss Ware tabby cat, 13" high, c. 1900, which sold for £4,500 when it came up for auction.
Photo: William Hardie Ltd.

Fife's bouyant antiques trade is well supported through busy auction rooms in St. Andrews and Dunfermline. The latter was, in the mid-19th century, the world's greatest producer of damask table linen which has given rise to a considerable trade nowadays in fine examples of the fabrics. Dunfermline District Museum houses a major collection of material from this era, and is well worth a visit.

An interesting collection of Wemyss Ware which made prices ranging from £160 (vase, left) to £210 (heart-shaped ink stand third from left), and an unusual Irish linen hand towel made for Earlshall Fair, machine woven with black crows and windmills which realised £190 when sold by William Hardie Ltd.

Surprisingly, with its strong maritime connection, Fife is not as rich as you would expect in a seafaring artefacts and nautical instruments. However, they are to be found from time to time in shops dotted around the coast.

No mention of Fife would be complete without comment on its status as the home of golf. Each year St. Andrews attracts thousands of visitors to its world-famous courses. With a golfing history which stretches back 450 years, the town is without doubt a Mecca for every enthusiast who has ever cursed a bunker.

Just opposite the doyen of world golf, the Royal and Ancient Golf Club, the recently opened British Golf Museum traces the development of the sport through the ages right up to today.

With 15 museums, of both national and local importance, a wealth of historic buildings and castles, and many conservation villages and hamlets, Fife provides an enjoyable and stimulating experience on all levels.

The starting point of our 65-mile round trip is Dunfermline. Some 15 miles from Edinburgh across the Forth Road Bridge - the access point for all Fife outings - Dunfermline is the birth place of Andrew Carnegie, a weaver's son who emigrated to the New World and amassed an incredible fortune from the American steel industry, then gave away an estimated three hundred and fifty million dollars to become one of the largest public benefactors of all time. To this day Scotland is still reaping the benefits of this remarkable philanthropist's generosity.

The cottage in Moodie Street where he was born, has been carefully preserved, recapturing the atmosphere of the loom shop he knew so well as child. The Carnegie link is carried through to another of the town's museums, Pittencrieff House, an early 17th century mansionhouse which was converted to its present use in the 1920's with the aid of Carnegie funds. Set in a beautiful estate, the museum houses a major costume collection.

There is a glorious assortment of bric-a brac to be sifted through and antiques a plenty at nearby Aberdour, Burntisland, Kinghorn and Kinross. In Burntisland, Roger E. Shivas has tuned into one of the newest areas of interest - vintage radios and wireless sets. Whether you are interested in purchasing a reconditioned piece of nostalgia or having an old radio repaired or restored, he's the man to phone. Visits, however, are by appointment only.

Four miles north of Kinghorn, on the B925, is Auchtertool, where the substantial country home and workshops of one of Scotland's master craftsmen, Peter Nicholson, are situated. Over the years his skills have been employed on virtually every stately home and castle in Fife. When he is not restoring or regilding ancient roof beams and panelling, he finds time to take on reproductions of quality furniture to the finest standards.

Kirkcaldy, where the bracing sea air is still redolent with the peculiar odour of linoleum manufacturing processes, doesn't readily spring to mind as a centre for Fine Arts and Crafts. Yet that is exactly what it is.

Thanks to the forward-thinking municipal museum service, it has amassed one of the country's best collections of 19th and 20th century Scottish painters. In the Kirkcaldy Museum and Art Gallery, at the War Memorial Gardens, is a truly magnificent display of Scottish art which includes works by Raeburn, McTaggart, Peploe and the Colourists.

Crail Harbour at dawn.   *Photo: Scottish Tourist Board*

The museum's treasure house of surprises does not end there, however. It also has on permanent exhibition Scotland's most extensive collection of Wemyss Ware, including some of the rarest pieces ever made.

Kirkcaldy has three specialist shops to interest enthusiasts, so be sure to set enough time aside for the task in hand.

In Markinch, five miles away, (A92/B9130), there are two businesses of interest situated side by side and just a few minutes drive away is Falkland and one of the most spectacular Royal palaces anywhere in the country. Set in extensive and impressive grounds, this beautiful property, in the care of the National Trust for Scotland, holds much to inspire awe in visitors, and is renowned for its collection of important tapestries. Here too, buyers on the antiques and fine art trail will find two outlets to keep them satisfied.

Further round the coast, the poster in the window of the small, whitewashed sub-post office said it all: 'Be prepared to lose your heart forever'. If you come with us on our trip through The Neuk - that very special corner of Fife - you will soon come to understand the truth of that gentle warning.

The Neuk - or to give it its Sunday name, the East Neuk of Fife, is one of the most unspoiled areas of Scotland. It has an alluring charm which will draw you back again and again to the quaint, higgledy piggledy streets of its fishing hamlets dotted along a bracing coastline. Quite frankly, if there had been only one antique shop there, we'd still have found an excuse to engineer a trip around it!

However, there's no need to resort to such desperate measures. On this outing there's plenty to satisfy visiting dealers and collectors. There's a nice little cluster of shops in The Neuk itself, with plenty of others on the way, and numerous travel permutations, including the opportunity to take in St Andrews, with its wealth of calling points.

Taking the A915 we make our way to Upper Largo, where the village main street contains our first shop - a cut above the normal establishment, selling fine period furniture, china, glass, objets d'art and a selection of quality paintings and prints.

Pittenweem, with its distintive whitewashed little houses, many beautifully restored by the National Trust for Scotland, is the epitome of what a traditional fishing village should look like. In this picture postcard setting, two shops are to be found.

The bustling harbour, where early birds can observe one of the few remaining daily fish markets in the East of Scotland, is the last port of call in the village. Overlooking the quayside is one of Fife's quality establishments situated in a typically attractive Pittenweem building, complete with crow- stepped gables.

If the salt sea air has whetted your appetite, you'll enjoy Anstruther. At the harbourside there's the best fish and chip shop in the East! It's something of a legend with locals and visitors, alike. While you're in the area, take in the fascinating Scottish Fisheries Museum, with its wealth of exhibits concerning Fife's maritime tradition. Berthed in the harbour as a permanent floating museum is another piece of the Kingdom's seafaring past, the North Carr lightship - the last ever to operate off the Scottish coast. It afforded protection to sailors off the treacherous North Carr Rocks for more than forty years. Nearby are two shops choc-a-bloc with bric-a-brac.

Just ten miles North along the B9131 is St Andrews with much to offer the enthusiast. If you want to go on one of Britain's sunniest outings, forget traditional resorts such as Bournemouth, Eastbourne, Plymouth and the Isle of Wight. Pack a picnic lunch and head for St. Andrews.

It is one of those quirky statistical facts of Scotland's fickle weather patterns that the Royal and Ancient Burgh, and much of North East Fife, put Scarborough and Blackpool in the shade when it comes to notching up hours of sunshine, which is probably the reason why the university town has been so popular with visitors for more than a century.

St Andrews, of course, has a lot more going for it than a blink of sunshine and golden sands. The unique blend of medieval, Victorian and Edwardian streets give it an atmosphere all of its own and it is recognised as one of the great historic sites of Europe. A major ecclesiastical centre from the eighth century onwards, the town has always had a scholarly air, marked today by its famous university founded in 1410. It is a true university town, in the tradition of Oxford and Cambridge ... just as it is a true centre for antiquities, with many other points of interest in the surrounding countryside.

To the west along the A91 via the bustling market town of Cupar, are the villages of Collessie, Ceres and Newburgh, all offering more than enough to keep the average browser occupied for hours.

1 AILSA'S ANTIQUES AND BRIC A BRAC
113 High Street, Burntisland, Fife
KY3 9AA. Tel: 0592 872689.
Proprietrix: Mrs. Celia Fernie.
Bric-a-brac, small items for collectors.
11.30-13.00 and 14.15-17.00.
Wednesday: Half day.

2 ANTIQUES & GIFTS
26 High St., Aberdour.Tel:0383 860523.
China, pottery, glass, pictures, bric-a-
brac and decorative objects.
Tues-Sat: 10am-5 pm. Wed: Afternoons
only. Lunchtime closing.

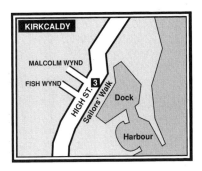

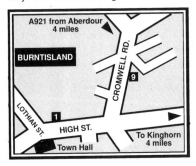

4 CASTLE RESTORATIONS
Auchtertool House, Auchtertool, by
Kirkcaldy, KY2 5XW. Tel: 0592 780371.
Proprietor: Peter D. Nicholson.
Antique furniture restorers.Commissions
undertaken. Boardroom, dining room
and banqueting tables made to any
specification. Seven days: 8 am-5 pm.

3 BOOK-ENDS
Sailors' Walk, 449 High Street, Kirkcaldy
KY1 2SN. Tel: 0592 205294
Proprietor: Mrs. A. Anthony.
Large, wide-ranging stock of antiquarian,
out-of-print & quality second-hand books,
cards, maps and prints.Tue-Sat:10-5pm.

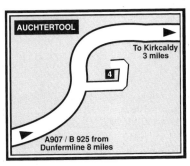

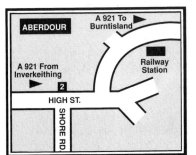

5 DUNFERMLINE AUCTION COMPANY (FIFE) LTD.
Loch Street, Townhill, Dunfermline
KY12 OHH. Tel: 0383 729899/727434.
Fax: 0383 729899
Regular auction sales every Tuesday.
General household, furniture and
effects. Antiques sales quarterly.
Telephone for details. All valuations.
Outside sales also conducted.

6 THE GOLDEN PAST ANTIQUES

90 Rosslyn Street, Kirkcaldy, Fife.
Tel: 0592 53185 / 260588.
Proprietrix: Fiona Campbell.
Victorian / Edwardian furniture,
fireplaces, jewellery, porcelain,and
interesting items. Kirkcaldy's longest
established antiques shop.
Tue-Sun: 10am-5.30pm. Closed Mon.

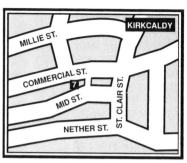

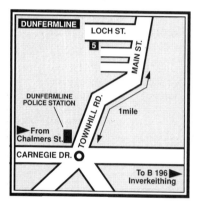

7 METHUSELAH'S

124 Commercial Street, Kircaldy, Fife.
Tel: 0592 261430. Eve. only.
Proprietor: John Sinclair.
British and European glass. Radios
(1930s -1960s). Period appliances, Art
Deco and collectables.
Mon: 10.30am-5.30pm. Tue closed.
Wed-Sat: 10.30am-5.30pm. Sun closed.

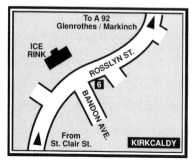

8 THE PEND

53 High Street, Kinghorn, Fife KY3 9UW
Tel: 0592 890207. Eve: 0592 890140.
Proprietrix: Mrs. B. Linton.
Tapestries, linen, wide range of furniture
and good quality, interesting china.
Open seven days: 10am-5.30pm.

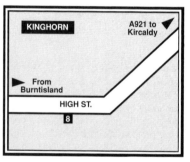

9 ROGER E. SHIVAS

Cromwell House, 34 Cromwell Road,
Burntisland, Fife KY3 9EH
Tel: 0592 872478. Eve. also.
Scotland's No. 1 for everything in vintage
wireless. Buying, selling, repairs, full
restorations. All work guaranteed.
By appointment. Please phone first.

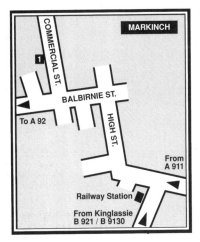

3 THE STABLES GALLERY

Back Wynd, Falkland, Fife KY7 7BX.
Tel: 0337 857272.
Proprietors: James and Ishbel Barnes.
19th & 20th Century oils & watercolours,
Georgian & Victorian furniture, Scottish
& studio pottery bought and sold.
Thu-Sat: 10.30am-5pm. Sun: 11.30am-
5pm. Winter: Sat & Sun only 11.30 am-
5pm. And by appointment .

4 TUDOR HOUSE ANTIQUES

South Street, Milnahort, by Kinross,
KY13 7XA.
Tel: 0577 863185.
Proprietor: John Neville.
Pine and good quality Georgian to
Edwardian furniture and other small
items.
Tues-Fri: 1-5pm; Sat: 10am-5pm;
Sun: 1-5pm. Or by arrangement.

1 GREEN'S ANTIQUES

15 Commercial Street, Markinch, Fife
KY7 6DE. Tel: 0592 754386. Eve. also.
Proprietor: Tom Green.
Good selection of antique and pre-1930
furniture; clocks; stripped pine; garden
ornaments. Mon-Sun: 2-5pm. Closed
Wed.

2 LODGE CURIOS

High Street, Falkland, Fife KY7 7AN.
Tel: 0337 857966. Eve. also.
Proprietrix: Aileen Davies
Diverse collection of antiques, bric-a-
brac, small furniture and extensive
range of china. Ever-changing selection.
Seven days: 10 am-5.30 pm.
Winter: 10 am-5.30 pm Fri-Mon.
Closed Tues, Wed, Thurs.

1 SQUIRREL ANTIQUES

13 Commercial Street, Markinch, Fife
KY7 6DE. Tel: 0592 754386
Proprietrix: Sheila Green.
Wemyss Ware, Scottish, English and
continental pottery and porcelain; small
decorative furniture; linen; collectables.
Mon-Sun: 2-5pm. Closed Wed.

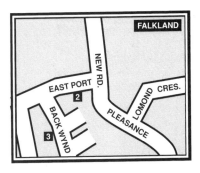

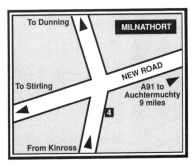

5 BYGONE DAYS

18-22 Cunzie Street, Anstruther, Fife
KY10 3DF
Tel: 0333 311970. Eve. 033 334 619.
Proprietor: Charles Trewern.
Bric-a-brac, china, furniture, old and
new. We buy as well as sell.
Mon-Sat: 10 am-5 pm. Sun: 1-4 pm.

6 THE LITTLE GALLERY

20 High Street, Pittenweem, Fife
KY10 2LA.
Tel: 0333 311227.
Proprietrix: Dr. Ursula Ditchburn-Bosch.
China, crystal, silver, brass, copper,
rustica, handpainted and other furniture,
paintings by contemporary artists.
Wed-Sat: 10am-5pm. Sun: 2-5pm.
(Winter: Thurs-Sun).

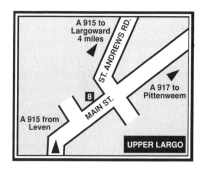

7 PITTENWEEM ANTIQUES AND FINE ART

15 East Shore, The Harbour,
Pittenweem, Fife KY10 2NH.
Tel: 0333 312054. Eve: 0333 310038.
Proprietors: K.M. McKillop and
D.O. Macneal.
Situated at picturesque harbour - we
specialise in original paintings, period
furniture, silver and objets d'art.
Seven days: 10am-5pm.
Winter: Closed Wed, Sun.

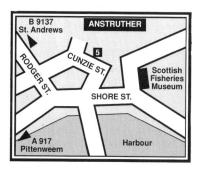

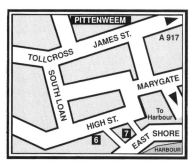

8 WAVERLEY ANTIQUES

13 Main Street, Upper Largo, Fife
KY8 6EL.
Tel: 033336 437. Eve. Also.
Proprietor: Dudley & Christina St. Clair.
18th and 19th Century period furniture,
china, glass, oil paintings, watercolours,
prints and objets d'art.
Mon-Sat:10.30am-5.30pm.

1 BILLSON OF ST ANDREWS

15 Greyfriars Garden, St. Andrews, Fife
KY16 9HG. Tel: 0334 75063.
Proprietor: David Waugh.
Specialising in antiquarian books, prints,
maps, county maps and sea charts,
exclusively of Scotland.
Weekdays: 10am-1pm; 2.30-5pm.
Closed Thurs.

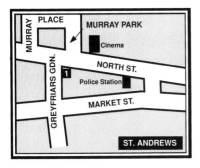

2 BYGONES ANTIQUES & COLLECTABLES

68 South Street, St. Andrews, Fife
KY16 9JT. Tel: 0334 75849.
Proprietor: Mrs. J. Guest.
General antiques including jewellery,
silver, bric-a-brac, linen, furniture etc.
Mon-Wed:10-1pm; 2-5pm.Thu: 10-2pm.
Fri-Sat: 10-1pm. 2-5pm; Sun: 2-5pm.

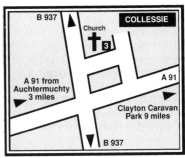

3 COLLESSIE ANTIQUES

The Glebe, Collessie, Fife KY7 7RQ.
Tel: 0337 810338.
Proprietrix: Mrs. Mary Maloco.
Antique furnishings, china, rugs,
paintings and individual modern
decorative and one-off items for the
home. Fri, Sat, Sun: 2-5 pm. And by
appointment.

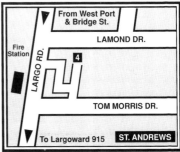

4 MACGREGOR AUCTIONS

56a Largo Road, St. Andrews, Fife
KY16 8RP. Tel: 0334 72431.
Proprietrix: Sandra Edwards.
Auction sales fortnightly (Friday).
Specialist antique sale quarterly.
Valuations for probate, insurance and
selling. Mon-Fri: 9am-4.30pm.

5 MAGPIE

28 Bell Street, St. Andrews, KY16 9UR.
Tel: 0334 74193. Eve: 0334 78391.
Proprietor: L. Jacobs. (Manager: A. Fraser).
Quality Collectables - furniture, porcelain, silver and jewellery - from Georgian to present day.
Mon-Sat: 10am-1pm; 2-5pm.

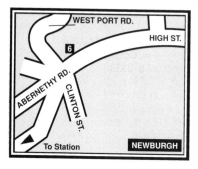

6 NEWBURGH ANTIQUES

222 High Street, Newburgh, Fife KY14 6DZ.
Tel: 0337 841026. Eve: 0337 840726.
Specialising in Wemyss Ware, Scottish watercolours, fine furniture 1780-1900 and objects of art. Mainly Scottish theme.
Open: 10.30am-12.00pm; 1.30-5.00pm.

7 A. & M. SPROSON

The Kirkhill Workshop, Gregory Place, St. Andrews, Fife KY16 9PU.
Tel: 0334 74249.
Quality picture-framing service.
Publishers of prints of local scenes.
Weekdays: 10am-12.30pm; 2-5pm.
Sat: 10am-12.30pm.

8 STEEPLE ANTIQUES

38 Main Street, Ceres, Fife.
Tel: 033 482 553. Eve. also.
Proprietrix: Elizabeth Hart.
Large selection of porcelain, silver, small furniture, bric-a-brac. Specialist in Victorian tableware, linen and cutlery.
Open six days: 2-5 pm. Closed Wed.

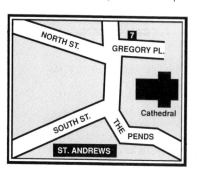

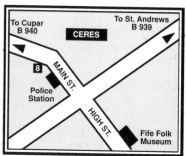

magine discovering a town where every second street contained a shop to tempt and tantalise the collector... a town where dozens of specialists covering the widest spectrum of trading activities, were all to be found within walking distance of each other. It might sound too good to be true, but that's the picture in Glasgow's wonderful city centre.

With a quite dazzling array of interesting stock available, the sheer breadth and variety proves to be a constant magnet to visiting dealers, serious collectors, keen specialists and enthusiastic amateurs alike. And in the pages which follow we will lead you to those same attractions in the auction rooms, private galleries, antique centres, shops and warehouses, bric-a-brac basements and curio corners to be found in this happy hunting ground.

The city centre bristles with galleries and, with Scottish art enjoying unprecedented attention from around the world, many of the country's top dealers have premises offering the very cream of the crop from well established figures to up-and-coming names.

The city's West End, with its cosmopolitan atmosphere and bustling streets, offers a fabulous diversity of browsing opportunities to keep

A three-legged Dunmore Pottery toad, 12" high, c.1890, which sold for £900 when auctioned William Hardie Ltd.

collectors and trade buyers well occupied. And, those with a love of antiquities who wish to look and learn, will also be richly rewarded.

Thousands of visitors regularly head this way to view the impressive exhibits in Glasgow's Museum of Transport, housed behind the Victorian splendour of the Kelvin Hall. Here, steam locomotives, gleaming fire engines and tramcars, horse-drawn carriages, vintage and veteran motors, penny farthing bicycles, old motor bikes and steam driven traction engines provide a fascinating experience for young and old alike.

The Kelvingrove Art Gallery and Museum - one of Glasgow's great visitor attractions - lies just across the way. Make sure you have two hours to spare in this vast treasure house ... and try to set some time aside too, for the nearby Hunterian Museum and Art Gallery where you will find the largest single collection of Whistler paintings in the world (over eighty exhibits), and the remarkable Mackintosh House - a reconstruction of the Glasgow home of Charles Rennie Mackintosh containing over sixty pieces of furniture and some six hundred of the architect's drawings, watercolours and designs.

But, let's get back to the heart of the matter to discover what this market place has to offer to those on the lookout for an investment or a bargain. Many of the shops and galleries are to be found in nice little clusters, especially around Great Western Road, Park Road, West Princes Street and Gibson Street, so leave your car in one of the pay-and-display areas and walk, if you want to avoid a parking ticket from the traffic wardens who patrol these parts.

There is much to choose from in the various trading activities of the area's antiques outlets and many of the dealers have carved out a special niche to attract those with particular needs.

On the busy South Side too, renowned for its fine spread of public parks, you'll find the city's biggest single crowd puller - the exceptional Burrell Collection. The remarkable custom-built repository with its eight thousand art treasures would, of course, be reason enough for taking a jaunt across the River Clyde. But, whatever you do, don't be tempted to

A Dunmore Pottery model of an owl, 16 cm, high which attracted a top bid of £1,000 in auction. Photo: William Hardie Ltd.

confine your wanderings to the grounds of Pollok Estate.

For, with a wide variety of attractions scattered around the area, including a healthy mix of antiques shops, private galleries and specialist traders, there is much to see and do.

Pollok House itself, just a stone's throw from the Burrell complex, will give hours of pleasure to those who wish to view the elegantly furnished rooms of the 18th century mansion. And, in nearby Bellahouston Park, a new attraction is set to grab a sizeable slice of the limelight. Undoubtedly one of the most important properties to be built in Glasgow for many years, the Art Lover's House, designed by Charles Rennie Mackintosh some ninety years ago, has finally materialised.

The extraordinary £2.4 million project took almost four years to complete as the plans, perspective and elevations were meticulously interpreted and brought to life. The elaborate external stone carvings and fabulous art nouveau interiors have been faithfully constructed to the last detail and the Music/Drawing room alone, with furnishings and carved wood panels all hand made by Barrhead cabinetmakers, Piers Kettlewell, will have devotees of the Mackintosh style drooling with delight.

Enthusiasts with shopping on their minds should head for the vicinity of Queen's Park and the bustling thoroughfares around its perimeter.

Mainstream antiques dealerships may be thin on the ground on the east side of the city ... yet each week, hundreds of hopeful collectors and visiting traders head to these very parts to savour the atmosphere of the world-famous Barras weekend market in Gallowgate.

Our favourite weekend pastime is to join the crowds which throng the bustling streets, lanes, courtyards and markets of The Barras. Over the years, countless treasures have been discovered among its junk stalls, but in these post-Negus times, you have to have your wits sharpened and be blessed with some good fortune if you hope to come away with a real prize find. In the good old days before Going For A Song set television viewers searching through cupboards and attics for valuables, it was not unusual for pieces of Clarice Cliff or Charlotte Rhead to find their way from jumble sales on to the traders'stalls.

Nowadays, with stallholders and public more knowledgeable in most matters, from Dr Who memorablia to Jessie M. King, it's a different ball game altogether but just as much fun as ever it was for those who rise to the challenge of pitting their wits against the trade - and rival bargain hunters.

The attractive fluted basket (centre) sold for £580 when this group of Wemyss Ware was auctioned by Christie's.

Above all, try to get there early. Many traders start setting up their stalls at 9am and the bulk of the wheeling and dealing takes place between then and ten o'clock.

To avoid disappointment, try to keep an open mind and be prepared for surprises. Another lesson we have learned is never to follow the same week-in, week-out routine. New faces regularly pop up with a fresh van load of wares to sell, so check out the out-of-the-way lanes, upper floors and hidden corners for new opportunities.

Our favourite haunts are Quinn's Antiques Arcade in Stevenson Street (things are bad if you come away from here without having spent just a few pounds); and - just across the street - The Square Yard, where Steven Currie keeps the pop, film and television memorabilia fans happy. Here, you will also find a nice selection of bakelite telephones, old toys and games and dozens of collectable records, annuals and comics to choose from.

There is plenty of car parking space available around the main market areas but, on Sundays in particular, when large crowds flock to the vicinity, it can sometimes be difficult to find a handy spot. One other word of caution: While most established dealers will be happy to accept personal cheques, the real currency of The Barras is hard cash.

A few miles south of the city, is the old market town of Lanark which is well worth a visit and should keep the antiques enthusiasts satisfied too.

1 E.A. ALVARINO ANTIQUES

203 Bath Street, Glasgow G2 4HZ. Tel: 041 221 1888. (Also at 86 Mains Road, Fairlie, Ayrshire).
Selection of good quality general stock including furniture, ornaments, pictures, instruments and objets d'art.
Mon-Fri: 11am-5pm. Sat: 10.30am-1pm.

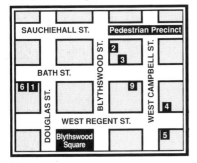

2 ROGER BILLCLIFFE FINE ART LTD.

134 Blythswood Street, Glasgow G2 4EL. Tel: 041-332-4027.
Proprietor: Roger Billcliffe.
Scottish painting, sculpture, ceramics, jewellery and glass from 1900 to the present day.
Valuation and Consultancy Service.
Mon-Fri: 9.30am-5.30. Sat: 10am-1pm.

3 CHRISTIE'S SCOTLAND LTD.

164/166 Bath Street, Glasgow G2 4TG. Tel: 041 332 8134.
Christie's only U.K. saleroom outside London. Free auction advice and Valuations for tax, insurance etc.
Open: 9-5pm (7pm selected Mondays)

4 CYRIL GERBER FINE ART

148 West Regent Street, Glasgow, G2 2RQ.
Tel: 041 221 3095 or 204 0276.
20th century British paintings and drawings including "Glasgow Boys" and Scottish Colourists.
Mon-Fri: 9.30-5.30pm.Sat: 9.30-12.30pm. (5.30pm during special shows).

1 GLENBURN ANTIQUES

203 Bath Street Glasgow, G2 4HZ. Tel: 041 221 3639.
Proprietors: Isla & Iona MacKinnon.
Silver, jewellery, porcelain, pottery and objets d'art. Samplers and Scottish antique items.
Mon-Fri: 10.30am-5pm.
Sat: 10.30am-1pm.

5 WILLIAM HARDIE LIMITED

141 West Regent Street, Glasgow G2 2SG.
Tel: 041 221 6780. Eve. also.
Fax: 041 248 6237.
Proprietor: William Hardie.
Auction sales; ceramics, silver, furniture etc. Valuation services; tax, insurance etc. Picture restoration and framing.
Mon-Fri: 9am-5pm. Sat: 10am-1pm.

6 PHILLIPS SCOTLAND

207 Bath Street, Glasgow G2 4HD. Tel: 041 221 8377.
Occasional specialist and regular general sales. Free auction advice from our Edinburgh and Glasgow specialists.
Mon-Fri: 8.30-5pm. Sat: 8.30-12noon.

7 SARATOGA TRUNK

57 West Regent Street, Glasgow
G2 2AE.
Tel: 041 331 2707.
Proprietrix: Cathie McLay.
Vintage clothing; table and bed linen;
lace and tapestries; Paisley shawls;
period and costume jewellery.
Mon-Sat: 10.30am-5pm.

8 STRACHAN ANTIQUES AT HERITAGE HOUSE ANTIQUES

Yorkhill Quay, Clydeside Expressway,
Glasgow.
Tel: 041 334 4924. Workshop 041 886
4214 or Beith (0505) 504939 (anytime).
Proprietor: Alex Strachan.
Late Victorian and Edwardian furniture,
particularly oak.
Mon-Sat: 9am-5pm. Sun: 12 noon-5pm.

9 TIM WRIGHT ANTIQUES

Richmond Chambers, 147 Bath Street,
Glasgow.
Tel: 041 221 0364.
Largest stock of decorative objects and
furnishings in Glasgow. Specialist in
silver, pottery, porcelain and glass.
Mon-Fri: 9.30-5pm.Sat: 10.30-1.30pm.

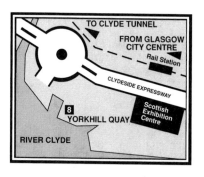

VINTAGE CLOTHING AT
STARRY STARRY NIGHT

19-21 DOWANSIDE LANE, GLASGOW G12
(OPPOSITE HILLHEAD UNDERGROUND) TEL: 041·337 1837

1 ALBANY ANTIQUES

1347 Argyle Street, Glasgow G3 8AD.
Tel: 041 339 4267.
Proprietor: P. J. O'Loughlin.
Fine Victorian and Edwardian furniture,
oriental ceramics and works of art.
Mon-Fri: 9.30am-5.30pm. Saturday/
Sunday by appointment.

2 DOWANSIDE BOOKS

Dowanside Lane, (opposite Hillhead
Underground), Glasgow G12 9BZ.
Tel: 041 945 2787.
Proprietrix: Louise Welsh.
History, politics, poetry, Scottish
literature, out of print, second hand,
antiquarian books, prints and maps...
Mon-Sat: 10.15am-6pm.

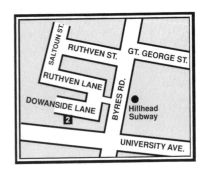

3 THE LOFT ANTIQUES

155a Queen Margaret Drive,
Glasgow G20 8XU.
Tel: 041 945 2211 or 041 339 3648.
Proprietrix: Henrietta Vallar.
Furniture, porcelain, brassware, silver,
pictures, shawls, carpets and linen.
Houses cleared or single items
purchased.
Thurs-Fri: 1-6pm. Sat: 12-6pm.

2 NOW & THEN

Dowanside Lane, (opposite Hillhead
subway), Glasgow G12 9BZ.
Tel: 041 339 1470.
Proprietrix: Elizabeth Anne Robb.
Enticing general collectables including
Scottish pottery, glass, paintings etc.
Come and browse, perhaps buy?
Mon-Sat: 11am-6pm.

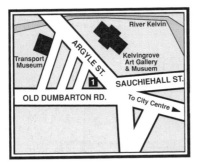

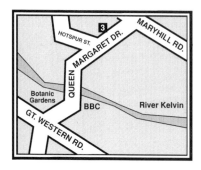

RETROUVIUS
14, Glasgow Street, Hillhead, Glasgow
G12 8JG.
Tel: 041 334 0086.
Proprietors: A. Hills & M. Speake B Arch.
Reclaimed architectural items from
complete interiors to door knobs. Interior
design consultation and sourcing service.
By appointment only.

2 STARRY STARRY NIGHT
19/21 Dowanside Lane, Glasgow G12.
Tel: 041 337 1837.
Vintage clothing from Victorian era to
1960's. Antique textiles, shawls and
linen.
Mon-Sat: 10am-5.30pm.

*Yesteryear Costume
and Textile Centre*   Cathie McLay's
Saratoga Trunk

57 WEST REGENT STREET, GLASGOW G2 2AE, TELEPHONE 041-331 2707

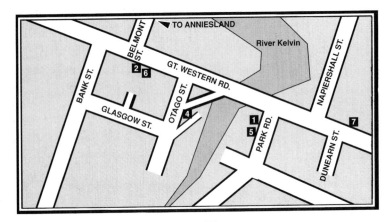

1 ALL OUR YESTERDAYS
6 Park Road, Kelvinbridge, Glasgow G4
Tel: 041 334 7788.
Proprietrix: Susie Robinson.
Old fashioned and over stuffed with
incredible finds! We've either got it or
we'll find it! Also Prop Hire.
Mon-Thu: 11am-5.30pm.
Fri-Sat: 10am-5pm. Or by appointment.

2 CALEDONIA BOOKS
483 Great Western Road, Glasgow.
Tel: 041 334 9663.
Proprietrix: Maureen Smillie.
Scottish, literary, fiction, art, poetry, film,
TV, sport, gardening, natural history and
reference books. Mon-Sat: 10.30-6pm.

3 FINNIE ANTIQUES
First Floor, 100 Torrisdale Street,
Glasgow G42.
Tel: 041 423 8515. Eve: 041 942 5744.
Proprietor: Bruce W. Finnie.
Antique to 1930's furniture and objets
d'art. Also specialising in architectural
items of interest including stained glass.
Mon-Fri: 10am-4.30pm.

4 GREAT WESTERN AUCTIONS LTD.
29/37 Otago Street, Glasgow G12 8JJ.
Tel: 041 339 3290.
Proprietrix: Anita Manning.
Jewellery, silver, EPNS, paintings,
ceramics, objets d'art, curios, antique/
general furniture.
Special quarterly paintings sale.
Mon-Fri: 9am-5pm.
Fortnightly Saturday Sale: 11am
(viewing previous Fri 10am-7.30pm).

5 LANSDOWNE ANTIQUES
10 Park Road, Kelvinbridge, Glasgow.
G12 8NX. Tel: 041 334 8469.
Proprietrix: Lynda Henderson.
Interesting old beds and fine furniture.
Mon-Sat: 10.30am-6pm.

6 JEAN MEGAHY
481 Great Western Road, Glasgow
G12 8HL. Tel: 041 334 1315.
Proprietor: F. J. Halliday.
Georgian, Victorian and Edwardian
furniture; porcelain, silver, brass and
EPNS wares.
Mon-Fri: 10am-5pm. Sat: 10am-1pm.

7 SOMETHING SPECIAL

240 Great Western Road, Glasgow
G4 9EJ. Tel: 041 332 5677.
Proprietors: Ian & Marie Winter.
Large stock genuine Victorian,
Edwardian antique & reproduction pine
furniture. Fire Surrounds, inserts, tiles
and accessories for the discerning buyer.
Mon-Sat 10-5.30pm.Sun: 12-5pm.

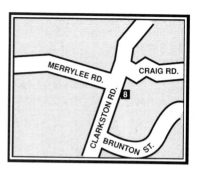

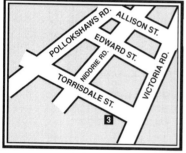

8 WAVERLEY ANTIQUES

219 Clarkston Road, Glasgow.
Tel: 041 633 2577.
Proprietors: R. & R. Shields.
Clocks, watches, Victorian and
Edwardian furniture, fine china, pottery
and bric-a-brac.
Tues-Sun: 9.30am-4.30pm.
Closed all day Monday.

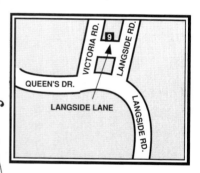

9 WEST OF SCOTLAND ANTIQUE CENTRE

Langside Lane, 539 Victoria Road,
Queens Park, Glasgow G42 8BN.
Tel: 041 422 1717.
Antique Georgian, Victorian, Edwardian
quality reproduction pine furniture.
Fireplaces, porcelain, brass etc.
10,000 sq. ft. Ever changing stock.
Mon-Sat: 9.30am-5.30pm. Sun:12-5pm.

1 ARTHUR E. COLLINS & SON LTD.

114 Trongate, Glasgow G1 5EN.
Tel: 041 552 0489.
Auctions (Tues, Wed, Thurs).
Antique and modern jewellery, furniture,
porcelain, silver, electrical, photographic
and sporting goods.Mon-Fri: 9-4.45pm.

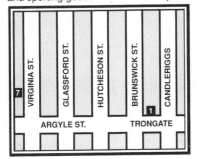

2 JO-EL ANTIQUES

Unit 3, King's Court Antique Centre,
Kings Street, Glasgow G1 1TU.
Tel: 041 552 7856.
Proprietors: Effie & Joan.
Fine antique and modern jewellery,
linen, lace and period clothing, Paisley
shawls, furniture, porcelain, silver, brass
and paintings.Tues-Sun: 10am-5pm.

3 ROBERT McTEAR & CO. (AUCTIONEERS) LTD.

6 North Court, St Vincent Place,
Glasgow G1 2DS. Tel: 041 221 4456.
Proprietors: I.F. Adamson, S.G. Clark.
Weekly Friday sales of antique furniture,
jewellery, silver, porcelain, at 10.30am.
Valuations. Regular special antique
sales each month. Telephone for
details. Mon-Fri: 9am-5pm.

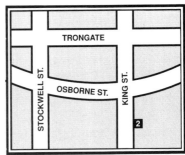

4 RELICS

The Square Yard, Stevenson St. West,
The Barras Market, Glasgow G40.
Tel: 041 357 4486 (24hours).
Proprietor: Steven Currie.
Telephones, radios, appliances, toys,
pop/T.V./film memorabilia, records,
annuals/comics, signs, advertisements,
packaging. Valuations. Sat-Sun:10-5pm.

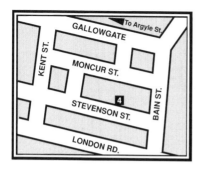

7 THE TREASURE BUNKER

Unit 16, Virginia Street, Glasgow
G1 1TU.
Tel: 041 552 4651. Eve: answering
machine.
Proprietor: K. Andrew.
Good quality militaria, specialising in
2nd World War German miltaria,
Victorian headress, medals and Scottish
items.
Mon-Sat: 11am-5pm.

5 FRANK RUSSELL & SON ANTIQUES

1 Rutherglen Road, Shawfield, Glasgow
Tel: 041 647 9608 or 0236 736385.
Fax: 0236 733772. TRADE ONLY.
Twenty year's shipping experience.
Furniture, old shop fittings, wall
panelling and all general antiques.
By telephone appointment.

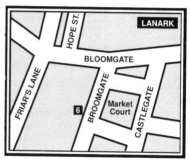

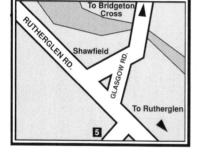

8 WOOLFSONS OF JAMES STREET

59/73 James Street, Glasgow G40 1BZ.
Tel: 041 554 7281.
10,000 sq. ft. showroom of general
antiques, including furniture, porcelain,
pictures, objet d'art etc.
Mon-Sat: 9.30 am-5pm.
Sun: 12noon-5pm.

6 THE STUDIO ANTIQUES

14 Broomgate, Lanark ML11 9EE.
Tel: 0555 664248.
Proprietrix: Marie Lezar.
Antique furniture, china, glass,
etchings,mirrors, bric-a-brac etc.
Open: 10am-5pm.

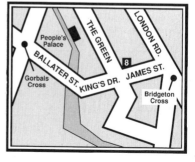

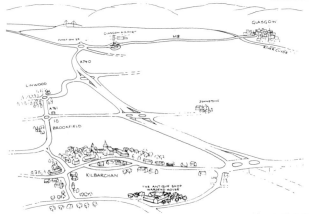

hen Cyril Rock commissioned a stoneware vase from the Cornish potter, Bernard H. Leach for the princely sum of £50 in the 1950s, he could not have imagined in his wildest dreams, the importance of his purchase. While his contemporaries in public museums and art galleries up and down the country were still looking to the past in their endeavours to complete civic collections, the director of Paisley Museum and Art Galleries had cast his eyes to the future.

In the months and years that followed, he researched his subject, made contact with leading craftsmen and women in their studios, visited top galleries to view their work ... and single-handedly amassed what is now recognised as a collection of studio ceramics of international importance.

That Leach pot alone might fetch up to £5,000 if it was ever to find its way on to the open market, and with selected pieces from Lucie Rie (whose work regularly commands four and sometimes five figure sums) and Hans Coper (who recently topped £80,000 mark) also strongly featured in the Paisley collection, it is easy to understand why students from around the world regularly visit the town's Museum and Art Galleries, now recognised as Scotland's main centre for the study of studio ceramics.

The town is, of course much better known for its world-famous thread-making and weaving traditions - and renowned for its production of fabulous Paisley shawls, which collectors are guaranteed to encounter on this trip to the towns and villages of Renfrew district.

The curators of Paisley's Museum and Art Galleries are justly proud of the town's collection of locally-produced shawls and are custodians of eight-hundred examples - the finest single assortment under one roof anywhere in the world!

The shawls act as a magnet for tourists and connoisseurs alike and when they arrive in Paisley they discover it is a township filled with hidden surprises.

Situated just a 15-minute drive along the M8 from Glasgow city centre it, is the largest town in Scotland, and an ideal stopping off place for anyone arriving at Glasgow Airport just a mile away. The town centre is dominated by an impressive 12th Century abbey, one of the few remaining examples from that time to have survived virtually intact to the present day, and which is still in regular use as a place of worship.

Paisley Central Library

In a building donated by the Coats Family in 1870, Paisley's 'Free Public Library' continues to serve ever more people in ever more ways. To the basic lending of books and answering of general queries have been added sections specialising in children's work, recorded music, and the town's history.

Audubon's Birds of America

John James Audubon (1785-1851) was an American ornithologist and artist born in Haiti. His father was a French naval captain. Audubon began to paint birds from life and in 1826 he came to Britain to seek a publisher. Lizars of Edinburgh initially began the engravings which were taken over by Havell of London. 'Birds of America' (1827-38) contains 435 plates. Sir Peter Coats donated a complete set in 4 volumes to Paisley Public Library.

The Central Library, High Street, Paisley, PA1 2BB, Tel: 041-889 2360
Opening Hours: Mon, Tues, Thurs, Fri: 10am-8pm; Wed & Sat: 10am-5pm
Reference Section: Mon - Fri: 9am-8pm; Sat: 9am-5pm

Department of Arts & Libraries, Renfrew District Counci

A Hans Coper pot from the Paisley collection. Photo: Paisley Museum and Art Gallery.

Visitors have recently been flocking in increasing numbers to another attraction, just a short distance away in aptly named Shuttle Street. Here, we find the award winning Sma' Shot Cottages which have been painstakingly restored by volunteers from the ranks of the Old Paisley Society. The former weaving cottages have been fully refurbished to recapture the lifestyles of those who once lived there.

Not surprisingly, Paisley shawls are frequently to be found for sale at local auctions and through the antiques trade in the area. One of the busiest auction firms is Andrew Moran & Son, whose Seedhill Road salerooms regularly attract private buyers and dealers. Bookworms should head for nearby Johnston Street, where the town's sole second hand bookshop is situated. The floor-to-ceiling shelves are bound to contain something to suit every taste and we have certainly spent many a happy hour browsing - and buying - here.

At Barrhead, three miles from Paisley, it's battered and tarnished items of metalware which find their way to a specialist in Main Street. The company is one of the few to be found in the West of Scotland who can undertake expert renovation of brass, copper and pewter. Plate-stripping is also available and the proprietors always keep a well stocked small showroom packed with bric-a-brac, furniture and, of course, metal wares.

Lugton lies eight miles to the west of Barrhead on the A736 and on the outskirts of the village, at Easter Highgate, a young couple are carrying on the traditions of the woodworker. In these former farmyard buildings,

Kilbarchan's weaver's cottage. Photo: National Trust for Scotland.

the workspace is shared by a partnership of experienced hands which can be turned to everything from French polishing and rush and cane re-seating to the manufacture of stylish modern furniture.

The main focus of interest for the antiques hunter is centred on the picturesque one-time weaving village of Kilbarchan, some twenty minutes from Lugton. Reached more directly from Paisley (just ten minutes by car via the A737/B787), if we were to tell you that international buyers from Japan, Australia, Italy and France regularly make their way to Kilbarchan in search of rich pickings, you will understand why this has been a destination of some importance to dealers and collectors for some years. It is also a favourite haunt for interior designers on the look out for decorative and unusual furnishings.

One of the biggest and most highly regarded dealerships in the West of Scotland is to be found in Kibbleston Road just over a mile from the centre of the village. The country house and its courtyard outbuildings provide twelve rooms with a quite stunning array of contents for sale. A recent newcomer to the scene is to be found in the village's Steeple Street where a small gallery regularly features the work of leading contemporary artists. At nearby Johnstone, a real specialist has a massive warehouse of items salvaged from demolition jobs. The premises are frequently plundered by TV, film and theatre companies on the lookout for props.

Discerning buyers have for some time been beating a track to the village of Kilmacolm, ten minutes to the west of Kilbarchan on the A761, and at Bridge of Weir too, fine old fabrics, Paisley shawls and country antiques attract interest from a select band of followers at premises on an appointment-only basis.

1 BURNTHILLS DEMOLITION & ARCHITECTURAL RECLAMATION LTD. (Incorporating Scottish Teleprops)

Floors Street, Johnstone, Renfrewshire
PA5 8QS.
Tel: 0505 329644 / 328456.
Fax: 0505 325287.
Proprietor: J. M. Kinniburgh.
Flooring, doors, panelling etc. Also full range of props for sale/hire to TV, film, theatre companies. TRADE ONLY or telephone appointment.

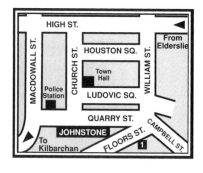

2 CPR ANTIQUES & SERVICES

96 Main Street, Barrhead.
Tel: 041 881 5379.
Brass, copper, spelter and pewter repaired and restored. Metal machining. Plating (including chrome) stripped. All antiques bought and sold.
Open five days 10am-1pm; 1.30-5pm.
Closed Tuesday and Sunday.

3 ANDREW MORAN & SON

"Andmor House", 6 Seedhill Road, Paisley PA1 1JS.
Tel: 041 889 4545. Fax: 041 848 7041.
Proprietor: A.C. Moran.
Regular auction sales of antique and Victorian furniture, pictures, plate and bric-a-brac.
Wed: sale day. Tues: preview.

4 WORDSWORTH & CO.

4 Johnston Street, Paisley PA1 1XG.
Tel: 041 887 7303.
Proprietrix: Susan M. Dennison.
Wide selection second-hand books.
Mixed general readers' stock.
Also fine art greetings cards.
Mon-Sat: 10.15am-5.45pm.

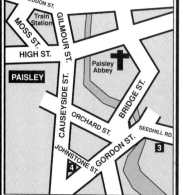

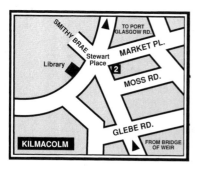

1 GARDNER'S "The Antique Shop"

Wardend House, Kibbleston Road,
Kilbarchan, Renfrewshire PA10 2PN.
Tel: 0505 702292.
Proprietors: George & Robert Gardner,
Large general stock of furniture,
porcelain, silver, pictures etc. including
Georgian and Victorian items.
Mon-Fri: 10am-1pm; 2-6pm.
Sat: 10am-1pm.

2 KILMACOLM ANTIQUES

Stewart Place, Kilmalcolm,
Renfrewshire.
Tel: 050587 3149.
Proprietrix: Mrs. Hilary McLean.
Fine quality Georgian and Victorian
furniture. Large selection jewellery,
silverware, porcelain and pictures.
All restorations undertaken.
Open five days: 10am-1pm; 2.30-
5.30pm. Closed Wed, Sun.

3 LIVING FURNITURE

Easter Highgate, Irvine Road, by
Lugton, Ayrshire KA15 1HZ.
Tel: 0505 850662. Eve: 850687.
Restoration and conservation. French
polishing, cabinet making, cane and
rush re-seating. Quality furniture
designed and hand made to customers'
specifications.
Open seven days: 8.30am-8.30pm.

■ MARJORIE McDOUGALL

Bridge of Weir, Renfrewshire.
Tel: 0505 612292.
Props: Marjorie and Sandy McDougall.
Antique bedsteads, textiles, Paisley
shawls, quilts, samplers, linens,
decorative furniture.
Please telephone for appointment.

4 STUDIO ARTS GALLERY

19 Steeple St., Kilbarchan, PA10 2FJ.
Tel: 0505 705167
Proprietor: Robert Mulhern D.A.
Contemporary Scottish painting and
sculpture, art books and cards,
children's books.
Wed-Fri: 1-5pm. Sat & Sun: 11am-5pm.

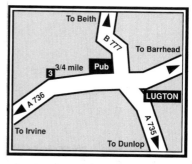

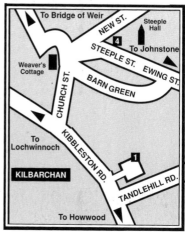

A fascinating selection of Tartan Ware featuring Bonnie Prince Charlie, Rob Roy and other Scottish themes. Photo: Christie's

Lochwinnoch Community Museum

As a concept, Lochwinnoch Community Museum represents the unique departure from the traditional local museum. Lochwinnoch has no permanent exhibitions; instead the gallery area features a series of changing exhibitions reflecting local history, culture and the environment. It is also the venue for exhibitions originating from the ideas and suggestions of the community itself.

Lochwinnoch Community Museum
Main Street, Lochwinnoch, PA12 4AB,
Tel: Lochwinnoch 842615
Opening Hours:
Mon, Wed, Fri: 10am-1pm, 2-5pm, 6-8pm
Tues, Sat: 10am-1pm, 2-5pm
Thur, Sun: Closed all day
Department of Arts & Libraries, Renfrew District Council

A Coastal Trip Through Inverclyde & Ayrshire

here are few pleasures more enjoyable than an exhilarating coastal drive along the Southern shores of the Clyde Estuary with its panoramic views across the Firth to the Gare Loch and Bute. It's a journey well loved by get-away-from-it-all-Glaswegians who, in days gone by travelled "doon the watter" in their thousands on board the famous steamers which plied between the Broomielaw and Ayrshire's many seaside resorts.

Enthusiasts, today, can still enjoy the sights and sounds of those halcyon days aboard the world's last ocean-going paddle steamer, Waverley, which in the summer months carries excited passengers down the Clyde, its paddle wheels thrashing the river into foam.

And, there are many maritime delights in store as we set off for the towns of Port Glasgow, Greenock and Gourock...and beyond to Largs, Fairlie, Saltcoats, Irvine, Prestwick and Troon. For, all of these are inextricably linked with seafaring.

In Port Glasgow (some 20 miles from Glasgow along the M8) there is a full-sized replica of the world's first ocean-going steamship, Comet, built by local shipbuilder John Wood in 1812. The boat's revolutionary steam engine owed much to the pioneering genius of another "local-boy" - the inventor James Watt, from Greenock.

In Greenock itself, there are ambitious plans to build a quayside maritime and immigration museum - and site an old-time sailing ship in one of the dry docks. A maritime theme runs right through the recently modernised exhibition area of the town's McLean Museum and Art Gallery in Kelly Street, with important displays of model engines, ships and navigational instruments. Prominence is also given to ceramics from the local Clyde Pottery which operated from 1816 to 1905, as well as Greenock provincial silver of the late 17th and early 18th centuries. The Museum is renowned for its fine collection of ethnographic artefacts and the Japanese section is exceptional in its quality.

Gourock lies just two miles west and on the way, it is worthwhile making a short detour to the top of Lyle Hill to enjoy the breathtaking views out over Cardwell Bay. At nearby Ardgowan too, there is an appointment-only chance to view high class antique stock while further opportunities to buy nice wares present themselves in Largs and Fairlie.

A Mauchline Ware transfer-printed money box depicting Glasgow Green and the Suspension Bridge. Photo: Kelvingrove Art Gallery and Museum

No summer is complete in these parts without a visit to nearby Kelburn Country Park with its superb gardens, nature walks, spectacular waterfalls and 1000-year-old trees. This is the family home of the Earls of Glasgow, and Kelburn Castle is open to the public for a limited period only in the spring.

A few miles down the coast, the antiques trail continues with interesting premises and a wide and varied stock in the aforementioned towns and - inland - another big dealership on the outskirts of Kilmarnock.

While prospecting in these parts, it is worth keeping an eye out for items of Mauchline Ware, some examples of which are highly prized by collectors around the world.

These charming little treen souvenirs, whether plain varnished wood, featuring transfers of local landmarks and beauty spots, or covered in tartan finish, were first produced in the 1860s when the Mauchline factory of W & A Smith began churning out the novelty gifts. Millions of pieces were produced by the factory until it was burned to the ground in 1933.

The range was ingenious and diverse, covering everything from buttons, napkin rings, egg cups, bookmarks and pin cushions to snuff boxes, thimble containers, darning mushrooms and stamp and cotton reel boxes.

◼ ARDGOWAN ANTIQUES

Tel: 0475 521226
Proprietrix: Lady Shaw Stewart.
Decorative antiques, mainly furniture
and ceramics.
By appointment only.

1 FAIRLIE ANTIQUES SHOP

86 Main Road, Fairlie, Ayrshire
KA 29 0AD. Tel: 0475 568613.
Proprietrix: Mrs. E. A. Alvarino.
Interesting selection of jewellery,
silverware, glass, china, objets d'art and
small items of furniture.
Thu-Fri: 12 noon-5pm. Sat: 11am-5pm.

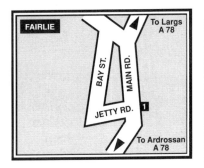

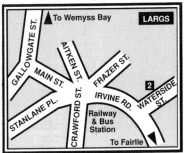

McLean
MUSEUM & ART GALLERY
Greenock

Displays feature local history
topics, ship and engine
models, maritime collections,
big game mounts,
ethnography and fine art.

15 Kelly Street,
Greenock

OPEN 10-12, 1-5 MON-SAT

Tel: 0475 23741

INVERCLYDE
DISTRICT COUNCIL

2 NARDUCCI ANTIQUES

57 Raise Street, Saltcoats A21 5J2 &
13 Waterside Street, Largs KA30 9LW.
Tel: 0294 61687 / 67137; 0475 672612;
Mobile:0831 100152.
Proprietor: G. Narducci.
Antiques, curios, large selection
furniture and shipping goods. Packing
and shipping anywhere. Road haulage
Europe. Houses cleared.
Largs: Tues, Thurs, Sat: 2.30-5.30pm.
Saltcoats every afternoon or by
appointment outwith.

3 JACKIE STEWART ANTIQUES

33/39 Townhead, Irvine, Ayrshire
KA12 OBH.
Tel: 0294 74074.
All antiques, furniture and bric-a-brac
bought and sold. Speciality: Maritime
instruments and fittings.
Mon-Sat: 10am-5pm or (TRADE) by
appointment anytime.

4 WESTWORDS

14 Newton St., Greenock. Tel: 0475 892467.

Proprietor: O. Dennison.

Wide selection general readers' books, fiction and non-fiction. Also fine art greetings cards .Mon-Sat: 9.30-5.30pm.

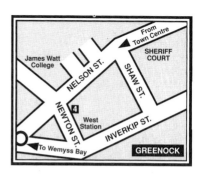

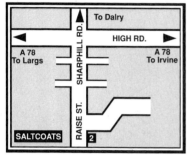

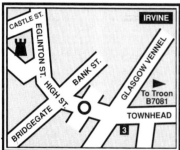

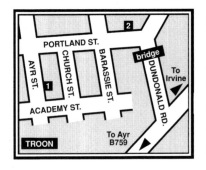

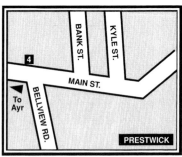

1 OLD TROON SPORTING ANTIQUES

49 Ayr St., Troon, Ayrshire KA10 6EB.
Tel: 0292 311822. Eve: 313744.
Fax: 0292 313111.
Proprietor: Bob Pringle.
Sporting antiques, especially golf art, golf memorabilia, piscatoriana, tennis, real tennis. Also general antiques.
Mon, Tues, Thurs, Fri: 9.30am-5pm.
Wed, Sat: half day closing.

2 ISOBEL PATTERSON ANTIQUES

125 Portland Street, Troon, Ayrshire KA10 6QN. Tel 0292 311615.
Many items of interest, including general antiques and bric-a-brac.
Antiquarian and second-hand books.
Open six days: 11.30am-5.30pm.
Closed Wednesdays.

3 Q.S. ANTIQUES

Unit 4, Moorfield Industrial Estate by Kilmarnock KA2 0DP. Tel: 0563 71071
Proprietors: John Cunningham and Douglas Johnson.
Antique and stripped pine furniture.
Reproduction farmhouse furniture makers and full restoration service.
Mon-Fri: 9am-5.30pm. Sat: 9am-5pm.

4 YER GRANNY'S ATTIC

176 Main St., Prestwick.Tel: 0292 76312.
Proprietor: Betsy Twelves-Dickson.
A treasure trove of collectables and antiques. Stained glass studio producing traditional and contemporary glass.
Restorarion. Mon-Sat: 10-6pm.

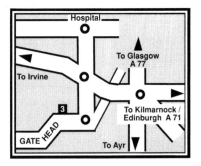

enture north into the heartlands of Stirlingshire or travel west from Glasgow to Dunbartonshire and the surrounding countryside around Loch Lomond and you are sure to sample a true taste of Scotland's many scenic delights.

...And if the scenery takes your breath away, then so, surely will the rich array of antiques and collectors' items to be encountered in the many shops along the way.

In Stirlingshire there are a hundred and one things to see and visit from castles and museums to ancient battlefields and historic pageants. Rugged Stirling itself, some 25 miles from Glasgow, sits proudly at the heart of Scotland's past. The spectacularly-sited castle where Mary Queen of Scots was crowned, dominates the skyline. It was a stronghold of the Stuart kings, a former seat of the Scottish Parliament and is today the regimental HQ of the Argyll and Sutherland Highlanders.

In the summer months, the town's ancient cobbled streets provide a stage for actors in period costume to re-enact scenes from the past, and the colourful programme includes a Ghost Tour through graveyards, hushed back streets and eerie buildings.

If we needed a good reason to go to Doune (just a short drive to the north) we could recommend a visit to its imposing 14th century castle or to the Earl of Moray's Motor Museum with its fine collection of vintage and classic vehicles. But there are antiques to be viewed here too as at

A group of Linoel and Elastolin toy soldiers which marched off with a bid of £330 when auctioned by Loves of Perth.

nearby Gargunnock and Dollar in neighbouring Clackmannanshire where visitors are also drawn each year to climb the picture postcard track up to spectacular Castle Campbell, perched high above its deep tree-covered glen.

Head west from Gargunnock to Buchlyvie, Balfron and Killearn and you will also find a remarkable variety of antiques and collectables in the shops situated in those rural communities, before making for Balloch and on to elegant Helensburgh and Garelochhead where further treats lie in store.

Helensburgh each year draws tourists from around the world keen to gaze in wonder at the art nouveau splendour of Charles Rennie Mackintosh's finest piece of domestic architecture - Hill House - which is open to the public thanks to the National Trust for Scotland.

We have spent many equally rewarding hours browsing through the seven thousand second hand and antiquarian publications for sale on the shelves of an excellent bookshop nearby.

THE BEST TIME
YOU'LL HAVE IN AGES!

Award-winning entertainment for everyone awaits you in Royal Stirling, Heart of Scotland, home of the young Mary, Queen of Scots, and ancient fortress of the Stuart kings. Stirling Castle, formidable seat of power and intrigue, proudly stands guard over a medieval town, steeped in folklore and tradition.

See what life was really like for Stirling's royalty and townsfolk, living side-by-side in its charming, cobbled streets. The unique Living History programme recalls tales of bygone days... Meet the colourful personalities who inhabited the beautiful Old Town – a cast of Historical Characters to entertain you with scenes of love, hate and revenge!

Experience the hustle-and-bustle of a Medieval Market, the sound of fiddlers, the fascination of a guided walk among the beautiful buildings of the Old Town and the mystery of the Ghost Walk. Soak up the atmosphere of a Ceilidh and enjoy the sound of Scotland's music, as pipers' traditional tunes fill the air around Stirling's citadel rock.

It's not the Old Town alone that displays the charm of Central Scotland's finest attraction – why not step aboard the Open Top Bus for a guided tour of all the other historical sites in the town.

A nation's heritage, its history and traditions, brought to life in great style in Stirling.

For further details, contact Loch Lomond, Stirling and Trossachs Tourist Board, 41 Dumbarton Road, Stirling. Tel: (0786) 75019.

ROYAL STIRLING...
WHERE HISTORY COMES ALIVE!

ROYAL STIRLING

KEY TO THE KINGDOM

1 "AMPHORA GALLERIES"

16 / 20 Buchanan Street, Balfron, by
Glasgow G63 0TT.
Tel: 0360 40329. (Eve. also.)
Main St., Buchlyvie, Stirling FK8 3LX.
Tel: 0360 85203.
Proprietor: Mr. Laurence Ruglen.
Extensive range of fine antique furniture,
upholstery, silver and porcelain, with
many decorative and collectors' items.
Mon, Tue, Thu, Fri: 10am-5pm.
Weekends and evenings by appointment.

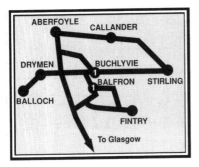

3 COUNTRY HOMES ANTIQUE FURNITURE CENTRE

Mains Farm, Gargunnock, by Stirling
FK8 3AY. Tel: 0786 860509.
Proprietor: Mr. A. Christie.
One of the largest stocks of restored
pine and country fine and period
furniture in Scotland. National
deliveries.
Weekdays: 10-5pm. Weekends:11-5pm.

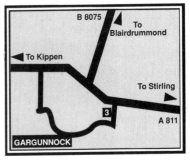

2 COUNTRY ANTIQUES

Main Street, Killearn, by Glasgow G63.
Tel: 0360 70215.
Proprietrix: Lady Edmonstone.
Small shop but with eclectic mix of
unusual and decorative items, wood,
silver, china, fabrics personally chosen
by Lady Edmonstone.
Mon-Sat: 9am-1pm; 2-5pm.

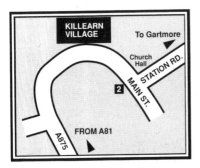

4 DENE HARD ANTIQUES

Dene Hard, Garelochhead,
Dunbartonshire G84 0EL.
Tel: 0436 810 669. (Eve. also.)
Proprietrix: Mrs. E. B. Ingleby.
A varied and interesting selection of
antiques always in stock.
Open five days: 10am 5pm. Closed
Mon, and Thurs. Will open by
appointment.

6 HILLFOOT ANTIQUES

36 Bridge Street, Dollar FK14 7DE.
Telephone: 0259 742495.
Eve: 0259 742228.
Proprietor: Scott A. Milne.
Selection of Victorian and Edwardian
furniture; paintings, fireplaces and small
pieces of china, porcelain etc.
Tue-Sat: 9am-1pm; 2-6pm.

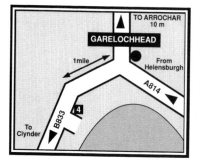

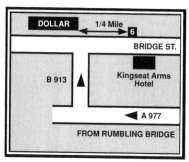

5 DOUNE ANTIQUES

40 Main Street, Doune FK16 6BJ.
Tel: 0786 841896.
Selecton of Georgian and Victorian
furniture; clocks, pottery, porcelain, bric-
a-brac and curios.
Open seven days 9am-5pm.

7 McLAREN BOOKS

91 West Clyde Street, Helensburgh
G84 8BB.
Tel: 0436 76453. Eve: 0436 820487.
Proprietor: G. Newlands.
Wide ranging stock of 7,000 plus books.
Scotland's leading dealer in naval and
maritime books.
Mon-Sat: 9.30am-1pm; 2-5.30pm.
Closed Wed (winter months) or by
appointment.

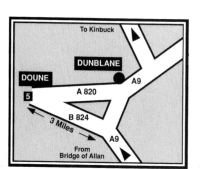

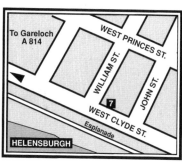

The imposing Doune Castle. Photo: Historic Scotland.

hen history and commerce meet head on, and intertwine down the centuries, you may be sure that there are rich pickings to be found by the generations who follow. And that is certainly the case with Perth.

The Fair City merits a full day's outing in its own right for collectors and dealers. Period furniture, provincial silver, quality glass, fine Scottish paintings - oils and watercolours - oriental works of art, decorative objects, rare and antiquarian books and prints, a multitude of collectors' items and enough shipping goods to keep the bigger visiting dealers happy... that's the story of this elegant gateway to the Highlands. And if you can drag yourself away from this exceptionally diverse antiques trail, there are scores of other interesting opportunities in the surrounding area.

One of the joys of prospecting in Perth itself is that all the shops are grouped within the town centre. We've also a small country jaunt North of the Tay, but more of that later.

For the moment, we're in the home of Monart Glass and fine antique silver. These local interest items are regular features among the Lots at the regular auctions.

It's a safe bet that much of the medium range to top quality goods to be found in the town's thriving antiques trade at one time or another has passed through local auction houses.

It would be unthinkable to leave Perth, and its classic Georgian terraces and crescents, without taking in something of its historic past. The great

Abbey at nearby Scone witnessed the coronations of all Scotland's kings from Kenneth MacAlpine in 838 to Charles II in 1651, and as a consequence Perth found itself constantly embroiled in the great moments of Scottish history. James I even made the town his royal residence and for a short time, until his assassination in 1437, it was effectively the capital of Scotland.

In modern Perth you can still start a bar room debate on the centuries old mystery surrounding the legendary Stone of Destiny on which Scotland's kings were crowned at Scone. It was stolen in 1296 by Edward I and removed to Westminster Abbey, but many locals believe the monks of Scone hid the original, replacing it with a replica for Edward to carry back to England.

The issue was clouded even further in modern times when Scots patriots staged a daring raid on Westminster Abbey and retrieved the symbol of Scotland's nationhood. The raiders, hunted high and wide by every police force in the land, managed to retain the Stone long enough for them to claim - when it was eventually recovered by the authorities - that a faithful copy had been taken back across the border.

A Victorian walnut bonheur- du-jour which sold for £2,250 when auctioned by Loves in Perth.

A fine collection of paperweights and ink bottles by Paul Ysart which realised £4,730 when auctioned in Perth. Photo: Loves Auction Rooms.

To this day. no-one knows where the real truth lies. The Stone of Destiny at Westminster could be a fake - or even a fake of a fake!

This is a county where the lore of glassmaking has been handed down from generation to generation, and collectors have not been slow to latch on to the particularly fine Monart and Vasart Glass produced here earlier this century. Monart in particular is now recognised as being among the most decorative of glassware made between the wars and, as such, commands increasing interest from serious enthusiasts.

Perthshire's earliest communities are those with ecclesiastical roots and Dunkeld, with it's impressive 14th century Cathedral ruins, is no exception. Today the town's distinctive whitewashed houses have been superbly restored by the National Trust for Scotland - and the village can be reached on that country jaunt we spoke of earlier. A rich seam of paintings, quality antiques and good old bric-a-brac lies in wait in the surrounding countryside at Bankfoot, Alyth, Pitlochry and Aberfeldy to the north and Crieff, Auchterarder, Comrie and Killin to the West.

1 ATHOLL ANTIQUES
80 Princes Street, Perth PH2 8LH.
Tel: 0738 20054; Eve: 0738 28524.
Proprietor: M. Gallagher.
Good quality Victorian and Edwardian
inlaid furniture suitable for Australian
and American buyers.
Mon-Fri: 9am-5pm. Sat: closed.

2 BEAUTIFUL HOMES
51/53 South Street, Perth PH2 8PD.
Tel: 0738 33335.
Proprietors: Mr. & Mrs. D.H. Sutherland.
Now on 2 floors. Flemish tapestries,
rosewood and mahogany furniture.
Hand-painted porcelain and lamps.
Made to order reproduction items.
Mon-Sat: 9am-5.30pm.

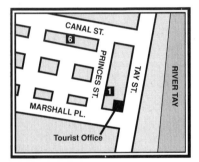

3 DESIGN INTERIORS
55 South Street, Perth PH2 8PD.
Tel: 0738 35360.
Proprietrix: Mrs. M. Blane.
Silver, porcelain, pottery, paintings,
furniture. A good stock of interesting
items and objets d'art. Mon-Sat: 10-5pm.

4 THE GEORGE STREET GALLERY
38 George Street, Perth PH1 5JL.
Tel: 0738 38953.
Proprietor: Susan Hardie.
20th century Scottish oil paintings,
watercolours, etchings and prints.
Mon, Tues, Thurs, Fri: 10am-5pm;
Wed, Sat: 10am-1pm.

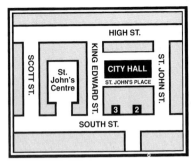

5 W. T. G. HENDERSON ANTIQUES & JEWELLERY
5 North Methven Street, Perth PH1 5PN
Tel: 0738 24836.
Jewellery, jewellery repairs, stamps,
coins, medals, silver, including
provincial; porcelain, glass and militaria.
Mon-Sat: 9am-5.30pm. Half day Wed.

6 LOVES AUCTION ROOMS
52/54 Canal Street, Perth PH2 8LF.
Tel: 0738 33337.
Regular antique and specialist sales.
Weekly sales (Fridays) of general
furniture. Valuations for all purposes.
Mon-Fri: 9am-5pm. Sat: 9am-12 noon.

7 IAN MURRAY ANTIQUE WAREHOUSE
21 Glasgow Road, Perth PH2 ONZ.
Tel: 0738 37222.
20,000 sq. ft. of antique, Victorian and
shipping furniture. Six established
dealers. Vast stock. Ample parking.
Mon-Fri: 9am-5pm.

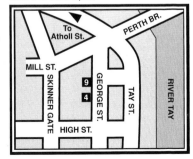

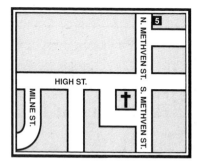

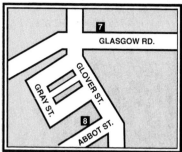

⑧ PERTH BOOKSHOP
3a Abbot Street, Craigie, Perth
PH2 OEB. Tel: 0738 33970.
Proprietor: Leslie J. W. Fraser.
Antiquarian/out of print books on most
subjects (mostly non-fiction). Also 19th
Century local prints.
Mon, Tues, Thurs, Fri: 10am-5pm.
Winter hours: (Jan-Mar)
Thu-Sat:10am-5pm.

⑨ ROBERTSON & COX
60 George Street, Perth PH1.
Tel: 0738 26300.
Proprietor: Michael Cox.
19th and 20th century British paintings;
period furniture, oriental rugs and small
decorative antiques.
Mon, Tues, Thurs, Fri: 10am-1pm;
2-5pm. Sat: 10am-1pm.

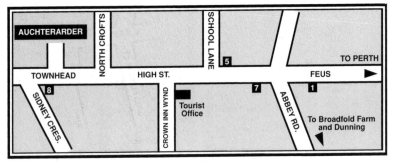

1 ANTIQUES AND THINGS
44 Feus, Auchterarder, Perthshire,
PH3 1DG.
Tel: 0764 663375.
Proprietors: Brian and Jill Baynham.
Old golf clubs and memorabilia, small
general antiques and collectors' items.
Mon-Sat: 9am-6pm.

2 THE COACH HOUSE
Dundas Street, Comrie, Perthshire
PH6 2LN.
Tel: 0764 670765.
Proprietrix: Mrs Mary Chilcott.
Early 19th century and Scottish
ceramics; Coalport, Spode, Ridgway,
Ironstone. Small silver, plate, bric-a-
brac.
Open: 10.30am-12.30pm; 2.30-5pm.
Closed Wed. and Sun. (Or by
appointment).

3 SONIA COOPER
19 Bridgend, Aberfeldy, Perthshire
PH15 2DF.
Tel: 0887 820266. Eve: 0887 820992.
China, glass, cutlery, prints, boxes,
pottery, metalware, curios and other
collectables, even bric-a-brac!
Summer: Mon, Tue Thu, Fri,Sat.
Winter: Thu, Fri, Sat; 11am-4pm.

4 MAUREEN H. GAULD
Craiglea, Main Street, Killin, Perthshire
FK21 8TE.
Telephone: 0567 820475.
Eve: 0567 820605.
General antiques, 18th-20th century
furniture, paintings, etchings, silver,
porcelain, glass, etc.
Mon-Sat: 10am-5pm. Mar-Oct. incl.

5 PAUL HAYES GALLERY
71 High Street, Auchterarder, Perth
PH3 1BN.
Tel: 0764 662320.
Est. 1962. 19th and 20th century
paintings, specialising in quality Scottish
and English marine and landscapes.
Mon-Sat: 10am-1pm; 2-5pm.
Closed Wed, Sun.

6 WILLIAM NEIL & SON
(CRIEFF) LTD.
22 Galvelmore Street, Crieff, Perthshire,
PH7 4DN.
Tel: 0764 653276.
Proprietor: Mr G.R. Spencer.
Auctions every three weeks of antique,
reproduction furniture, and general
effects. Valuations of all classes.
Mon-Fri: 8.30am-5pm.Sales Weds.
Viewing Tuesday 8.30am-6pm.

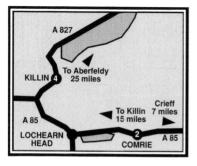

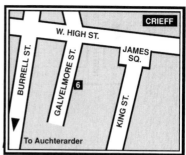

7 OLD ABBEY ANTIQUES LTD.

4 High Street, Auchterarder,
Perthshire PH3 1DF.
Tel: 0764 664073.
Proprietor: G. M. Cockain.
Furniture, silverware, ceramics, glass,
prints, paintings, curiosities and large
variety small items. The antique
general store.
Mon-Fri: 11am-5.30pm.
Sat: 11am-5.15pm.

8 K. STANLEY & SON

20 Townhead, Auchterarder PH3 1AH.
Tel: 0764 662252. Eve: 041 357 5592.
Proprietor: C.M. Kasiewicz.
Large Stock. General antiques and
furniture, objets d'art. Est. 35 years.
Mon-Sat: 10am-1pm; 2-5pm.

9 THE STRATHTAY BOOKSHOP

8 Dunkeld Street, Aberfeldy, Perthshire
PH15 2DA.
Tel: 0887 829519.
Proptietors: Barry and Theresa Dunford.
Scottish, literature, travel, natural
history, biography, world religions,
alternative health, environmental. New
books at reduced prices.
Mon-Sat: 10.30am-5pm. Closed some
Mons. and Weds. in Winter.

10 TIMES PAST ANTIQUES

Broadfold Farm, Auchterarder,
Perthshire PH3 1DR.
Tel: 0764 663166.
Proprietor: J. M. Brown.
One of the largest stocks of stripped
pine in Scotland. All work done on the
premises. Export packers & shippers.
Mon-Fri: 8am-5pm.
Weekends by appointment.

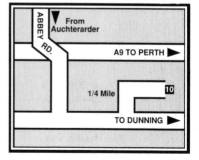

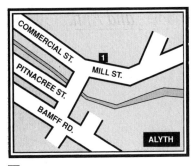

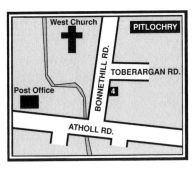

1 AIRLIE ANTIQUES
4 Mill Street, Alyth, Perthshire
PH11 8BJ. Tel; 08283 3101 / 2400.
Proprietrix: Jeanette McGill.
Antique pine, linen, lace, Paisley shawls,
pottery, textiles. Good selection of
country antiques.
Mon-Fri: 2-5pm (excl Wed). Sat: 10-5pm.

2 ANTIQUES & BYGONES
Tighvallich, Old Dunkeld Road, Bankfoot,
PH1 4AJ. Tel: 0738 87452.
Proprietor: William Wright.
Victorian & Edwardian oil lamps. Sale &
purchase. Restorations/repairs using
original parts. Phone for appointment.

3 ATHOLLBANK ANTIQUES
Main St., Bankfoot, PH1.Tel: 0738 87253.
Proprietors: John & Philomena Morrison
Smaller antique and decorative town
furniture, pine and country furnishings,
paintings, ceramics and decorative
objects.Mon-Sat: 10-6pm. Sun: 12-6pm.

4 BLAIR ANTIQUES
14 Bonnethill Road, Pitlochry,
Perthshire PH16 5BS.
Tel: 0796 472624. Eve. also.
Proprietor: Duncan Huie.
Furniture, clocks, Scottish paintings,
provincial silver, Scottish pottery and
continental porcelain.
Mon-Sat: 9am-5pm. Half-day Thursday.

5 PITCAIRN INTERIORS
Nether Pitcairn, Grandtully, by
Aberfeldy, Perthshire.
Tel: 0887 820217. Eve. also.
Proprietor: P.R. Mathis.
Furniture restorers and cabinet-makers;
upholstery, soft furnishings, antiques
and modern furniture bargains.
Mon-Sat: 8.30am-1pm; 2-6pm.

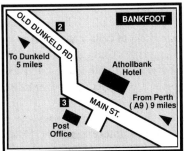

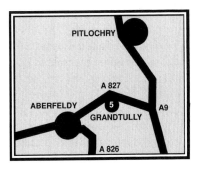

Whisky Galore, Good Food...and Antiques Too

here is something perverse about the suggestion that Scotland's national drink, the dram, if laid away like fine wine, will mature in value, if not necessarily in flavour. After all, whisky is made to be savoured not saved, and anyway, experts maintain that after a certain number of years it will gain little from being left untouched in its container. But bottles which have survived unopened for surprisingly long periods can nowadays command special attention from a growing band of enthusiasts around the world.

In 1991, a Japanese connoisseur shattered the world record for Scotch when he forked out £6,375 for a 60-year-old bottle of the Macallan and since then, rare finds unearthed from dark corners of cellars and storerooms are regularly offered for sale by leading auctioneers Christie's. When some of the rarest amber nectar ever to be offered for sale came under the hammer in their Glasgow saleroom, collectors clambered to get their hands on a cherished bottle or two.

Of the 446 lots offered, fourteen bottles recovered from the bowels of the shipwrecked SS Politician, captured the interest of the public, enthusiasts and the media alike. The Jamaican-bound cargo ship ran

Up from the murky depths... four of the bottles retrieved from the hold of the legendary SS Politician. Photo: Christie's

aground in the Outer Hebrides in 1941 and legend has it that her hold contained 250,000 bottles of Scotch. The entire episode inspired the late Compton Mackenzie to write his famous book on the subject and was later to feature in the much-loved Ealing comedy "Whisky Galore". Islanders were supposed to have been able to salvage 9,000 cases before the arrival of the Customs and Excise men. More recently, a commercial salvage operation was mounted - in 1990 - but only a small number of bottles were recovered. The bottles retrieved from the murky depths attracted keen interest from bidders with four of them eventually sold for £3,570...and the contents are undrinkable!

No tour of the Highlands would be complete without a taste of Speyside's Whisky Trail and in this section, we'll lead you to the very best distillery tour in Scotland where you can sample the world-famous single malt Glenfiddich. On any route north from Perth, the traveller is sure to encounter whisky galore along the way, but no warmer welcome will be found than that offered at the family-run Dufftown premises of William Grant & Sons.

Rest assured that there is much more in store than the whiff of roasted barley in these parts, however. A buoyant antiques trade has existed in the north-east of Scotland for many years and with an abundance of specialist traders in cities, towns and villages all over the region, a fascinating time is guaranteed.

Six of the bottles which attracted keen interest from connoisseurs when auctioned by Christie's.

The quality and interesting diversity of individual outlets makes the region a must both for the serious buyer and bargain hunter. Many of the shops carry an exceptional range of good period pieces while others feature a wonderful mix of mainstream antiques and general bric-a-brac. There are also some fine specialist craftspeople to be found offering expertise which is second to none.

The main cluster of trading activity is centred on the Granite City itself and the surrounding countryside, with points of interest en route at Dundee, Broughty Ferry, Brechin, Montrose and Stonehaven. Just inland from Aberdeen, there are antiques shops a plenty too at Dunecht, Kildrummy, Clatt and Torry. Those with a taste for good food would be well advised to time their trip to accommodate lunch at the fabulous Kildrummy Castle Hotel on the A97 just south of Mossat. Once sampled, never forgotten.

Peaceful Deeside first attracted Queen Victoria and Prince Albert in 1848 and the Royals have been heading to their Highland retreat at Balmoral ever since. Braemar with its world-famous Highland Gathering, held on the first Saturday in September each year, and the delightful Victorian town of Ballater, with Royal Warrant crests over the doors of most of its shops, provide a tranquil setting and set the scene for what lies ahead further to the north.

At Grantown-on-Spey and Dufftown (with that not-to-be-missed Glenfiddich guided tour) and in the towns of Forres, Nairn and Elgin, there is much to keep curious visitors well occupied. In fact the entire bracing north-east coastal shoulder from Inverness to Fraserburgh, is one of our favourite corners of Scotland.

No trip to the area would be complete without some time spent in hospitable Inverness. Those on the lookout for antiques and curios will not be disappointed as the variety of goods on display both here and at nearby Beauly and Avoch on the Black Isle, is rich enough to reward all tastes.

Further east, in Fochabers (almost an antiques village), Buckie and Portsoy, there are more attractions in store. Visitors planning to spend a night or two in the area should enquire about vacancies at the Stroma Guest House in Cullen where the welcome - and standard of home cooking - will make you want to stay on for a fortnight. Don't be tempted to eat out as this particular landlady knows how to put together such a mouth watering meal that she should feature in the good food guides.

Extremely rare Fine Old H.M.S. Scotch Whisky
from Bladnoch Distillery, Wigtown (c. 1870).
Photo Christie's.

A dream of a dram... The Real Mackay. Distilled and matured in Glasgow in the 19th Century, this surviving bottle sold for £700 when auctioned by Christie's.

PURE MALT
Glenfiddich
Scotch Whisky

You are invited to the home of traditional whisky. The Glenfiddich Distillery.

We would like to invite you to be our guest at The Glenfiddich Distillery. It was here on Christmas Day in 1887, under the watchful eye of William Grant, our founder, that Glenfiddich first ran from the stills. The Grant family have owned and managed the distillery ever since.

Glenfiddich is the only distillery in the Highlands where malt whisky is bottled on the premises – so you can see the whole original process for yourself, from the barley to the bottle. Then try a dram and discover the unique taste of the world's most celebrated malt whisky.

In our theatre we will introduce you to the history of Scotch Whisky and the heritage of the Highlands (and you can listen to it in English, French, German, Italian, Spanish or Japanese).

OUR OPENING HOURS
All year: **Weekdays:** 9.30am to 4.30pm
(excluding Christmas and New Year holidays)

In addition: Easter to mid October
Saturdays: 9.30am to 4.30pm
Sundays: 12 noon to 4.30pm

HOW TO FIND US:
The Glenfiddich Distillery lies on the A941, half a mile north of Dufftown, next to Balvenie Castle.

The Glenfiddich Distillery lies on the A941, half a mile north of Dufftown, on the north side of Balvenie Castle.

LARGER PARTIES
Parties of more than 12 people are welcome but please make advance arrangements by contacting:

The Visitors Centre
William Grant & Sons Ltd
The Glenfiddich Distillery
Dufftown, Keith
Banffshire AB5 4DH

Dufftown (0340) 20373.

We look forward to welcoming you.

William Grant & Sons Ltd

The Glenfiddich Distillery, owned and managed by the Grant family for five generations.

1 EDUARDO ALESSANDRO STUDIOS

30 Gray Street, Broughty Ferry, Dundee DD5 2BJ. Tel: 0382 737011.
Proprietor: Mr A. Paladini.
Traditional paintings & prints by leading Scottish contemporary artists. Framing and restoration. Scottish ceramics and crafts. Mon-Sat: 9.30am-5.30pm.

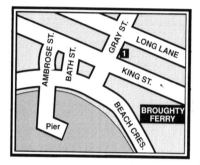

2 WESTPORT GALLERY/ WESTPORT FINE ART

48 Westport , Dundee DD1 5ER /
3 Old Hawkhill, Dundee DD1 5EU.
Tel: 0382 21751.
Proprietors: Sheena Livingstone and Grace McLean.
Collection of Victorian and Edwardian jewellery, antique furniture - pine, oak and mahogany. Interesting decorative objects, textiles, pictures, etc.
Mon-Sat: 9am-5pm.

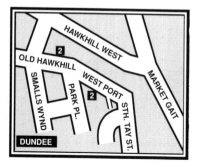

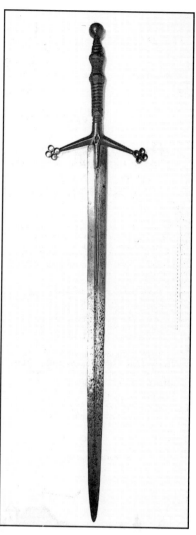

A very rare early 16th Century Scottish Highland Claymore, with a £6,500 price tag.
Photo: J.R. Webb Antiques.

99

1 ANGUS ARCHITECTURAL ANTIQUE COMPANY

Lower Balmain St., Montrose DD10 8BQ.
Tel: 0674 74291. Eve: 02413 271.
Proprietor: Mr. Leslie Morden.
Edwardian/Victorian fireplaces, brass &
iron beds, antique lighting and pine furn-
iture. Mon-Sat: 9-5pm or by appointment.

2 CASTLEGAIT GALLERY

12 Castle Place, Montrose, Angus.
Tel: 0674 73206.
Proprietors: Jack and Brian McCallum.
Quality picture framing. Good selection
of fine art prints, limited editions and
work by local artists. Mon, Tues, Thurs,
Fri: 9am-5.30pm. Wed & Sat: 9am-4pm.

3 COBWEBS

45 Barclay Street, Stonehaven AB3 2AX
Tel: 0569 64722. Proprietor: M. Black.
Everything from furniture to small
collectables including "arts and crafts",
Art Deco and country style.
Mon-Sat: 9.30am-5.30pm. Closed Sun.

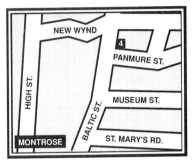

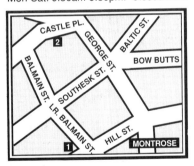

4 HARPER - JAMES ANTIQUES

25-27 Baltic Street, Montrose, Angus,
DD10 8EX. Tel: 0674 671307 / 77849.
Proprietors: D.R. and M.L. James.
Specialists in Georgian, Regency,
Victorian and Edwardian furniture,
porcelain and collectables.
Upholsterers, French polishers and
restorers. 2,000sq.ft. showroom.
Mon-Sat: 9.30am-5pm.

5 PRETTY OLD THINGS

15 Church Street, Brechin, Angus
DD9 6HB.
Tel: 0674 72609 (Eve).
Proprietor: Alison James.
Interesting selection of collectables,
jewellery, linen, china, glass etc.
Mon-Sat: 10am-4.30pm. Closed Wed.

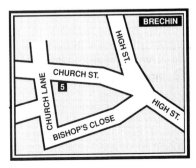

6 AWAKENING RESTORATIONS

Abbey Lane, Torry, Aberdeen AB1 3QR.
Tel: 0224 898778.
Proprietor: Angus M. Shepherd.
Furniture restoration and sales. "What is
left as a legacy, may we help save for
posterity". Mon-Sat: 9am-5pm.

7 THE McEWAN GALLERY

Glengarden, Ballater, Aberdeenshire
AB35 5UB.Tel: 03397 55429.
Proprietor: Dorothy McEwan.
18th to 20th century oils and
watercolours; prints; rare and elusive
books. Full advisory service.
Mon-Sat: 10am-6pm. Sundays: 2-6pm.

8 THE MAGIC LANTERN

Nether Corskie, Dunecht, Skene,
Aberdeenshire AB32 7EL.Tel: 03306 678.
Proprietors: Joyce and Philip Whyte.
Furniture and china, hand painted items
for sale. Commisions taken for painted
furniture and upholstery.
Tues-Sun: 10am-6pm. Wed: 2-6pm.

9 MOSSAT ANTIQUES

Bridge of Mossat, Kildrummy, by Alford,
Aberdeenshire AB33 8PL.
Tel: 09755 71300. Eves: 04646 309.
Variety of stripped furniture, Edwardian
and Victorian goods, lots of interesting
items from house clearances.
Thurs-Sun: 11.30am-5pm.

10D.C. ROGERS ANTIQUES

The Old Manse, Clatt, Alford, AB54 4NY
Tel: 04643 500. Proprietor: D.C. Rogers.
Wide selection of general antiques, dec-
orative items & country house furnishings.
Open: Anytime by prior arrangement.

11TREASURES OF BALLATER

1 Victoria Road, Ballater, AB3 5QQ.
Tel: 03397 55122. Eve:03397 56025.
Proprietor: Sheena Hepburn.
Wide selection furniture, silver, jewellery,
porcelain, clocks and general collectables.
Open: 10-1pm; 2-5pm.Or by appointment.

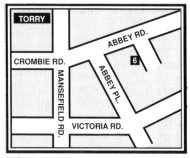

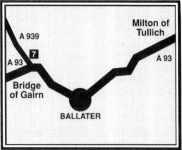

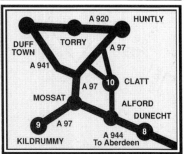

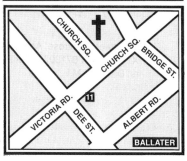

1 ADELPHI BOOKS/ ATTIC

24 Adelphi Court, Union Street,
Aberdeen AB1 2DL.
Tel: 0224 211233.
Propietor: A. Murray.
Antiquarian and Theological books.
Linen and lace, small items of furniture,
jewellery, bric-a-brac.
Mon-Sat: 10am-5pm.

2 JAMES L. ARCHIBALD & SONS LTD.

6-14 Great Western Road, Aberdeen,
AB9 2LQ.
Tel: 0224 596181.
Restoration of antique furniture, French
polishing, leather tops, upholstery repair
and re-covering.
Mon-Fri: 9am-5.30pm.
Sat: 9.30am-4.30pm.

3 BURNING EMBERS

165 King Street, Aberdeen.
Tel: 0224 624664.
Proprietor: J. Bruce.
Magnificent collection of around 100
restored Victorian and Georgian
fireplace inserts, surrounds, fenders,
etc. Unusual decorative items.
Mon-Sat: 10am-5pm, and by
appointment.

4 GALLERY / GRAY'S

41 and 41a Justice Street, Aberdeen
AB2 1HS.
Tel: 0224 625909 and 646438.
Four dealers specialising in furniture,
jewellery, paintings, bric-a-brac.
Collectables bought and sold.
Jewellery repair and valuation service.
Mon-Sat: 10am-5.30pm.

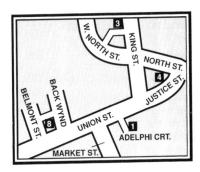

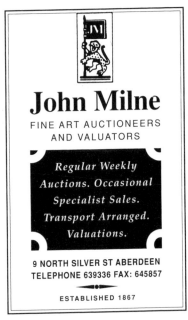

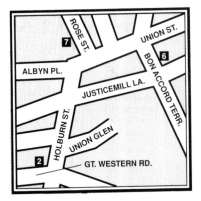

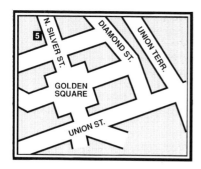

The Granite City

5 JOHN MILNE
9 North Silver Street, Aberdeen
AB1 1RJ.
Tel: 0224 639336.
Proprietor: Robert Milne.
Regular auctions every Wednesday at
10am. Occasional specialist sales of
collector's items. Valuations on request.
Mon-Fri: 8.30am-5pm. Closed Sat.

6 J.R. WEBB ANTIQUES
21/23 Bon-Accord Terrace, Aberdeen,
AB1 2DP.
Tel: 0224 586709. Eves: 0860 920215.
Wide-ranging selection of fine antique
quality jewellery, silver, furniture,
porcelain, Scottish weapons, objet d' art,
objet de vertu.
10am-6.00pm daily, except Wednesday
and half day Saturday.

7 COLIN WOOD
25 Rose Street, Aberdeen, AB1 1TX.
Tel: 0224 643019.
Scottish antiques, 17th/18th/19th
century furniture, paintings, Scottish
prints and maps, and objets d'art.
Mon-Fri:10am-12.30pm; 2.pm-5pm.
Sats: 10am-12.30pm; 2pm-4pm.

8 WILLIAM YOUNG (ANTIQUES) LTD.
1 Gaelic Lane (off Belmont Street),
Aberdeen, AB1 1JR
Tel: 0224 644757.
Proprietor: William Young.
Period, Georgian, 18th and 19th century
furniture, paintings and works of art.
Mon-Fri: 9.30am-5.30pm.

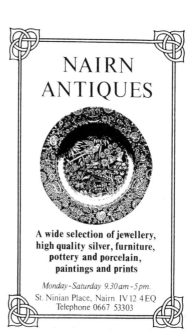

NAIRN ANTIQUES

**A wide selection of jewellery,
high quality silver, furniture,
pottery and porcelain,
paintings and prints**

Monday-Saturday 9.30am-5pm.
St. Ninian Place, Nairn IV 12 4EQ
Telephone 0667 53303

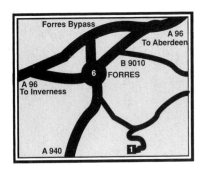

1 ALTYRE RESTORATION - GOLDEN ART

The Stables, Altyre Estate, Forres,
Morayshire IV36 0SH.Tel: 0309 672572.
Proprietor: Luigi Maria Villani.
Restoration:Painted/marquetry/fitted
furniture, marble, frames, objet d'art,
fittings - wood: Stains & finishes.
International service.
Mon-Fri: 9.30am-5.30pm. Week-end by
appointment only.

2 BROWSE AROUND ANTIQUES

19 South High Street, Portsoy,
AB54 2NT. Tel: 0261 42582.
Proprietors: Mrs. J. & Mr. J. Herbertson.
Selection of antique porcelain,
glassware, furniture, collectables and
stripped pine.
Open: Monday,Tuesday, Thursday and
Saturday 10am-5pm. Otherwise by
appointment.

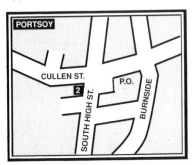

3 ALAN S. DUNCAN

The Smiddy, Drybridge, Buckie,
Banffshire AB56 2JL.
Tel: 0542 32271.
Large selection of antique furniture and
bric-a-brac. Doors and furniture
stripped and polished.
Mon-Sat: 10am-5pm. Closed Sunday.

4 BRIAN ALEXANDER FORSYTH ANTIQUES AND INTERIOR DESIGN

64 High Street, Fochabers, Morayshire
IV32.
Tel: 0343 821387 / 549313.
Country house interiors, fabrics and
decorative furnishings. Domestic,
contract and commercial refurbishment;
castles, hotels lodges.
Mon-Sat: 10.15am-4pm. Closed Wed.

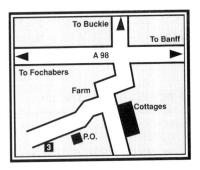

5 GRANNY'S KIST

Hadlow House, The Square, Fochabers,
Morayshire IV32 7DG.
Tel: 0343 820838.
Proprietor: Sheila Marny Hill.
Wide selection of kitchenalia, tools,
linen, old furniture, bric-a-brac, brass,
copper and collectables.
Mon-Sat: 10am-5pm.

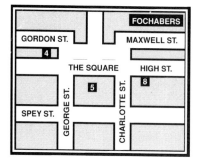

8 MARIANNE SIMPSON

61-63 High Stret, Fochabers, Morayshire
IV32 7DU.Tel: 0343 821192.
Reasonably priced second-hand and
antiquarian books, Maurice Walsh and
Dornford Yates a speciality. Free book
search.
Mon-Sat: 10am-1pm; 2-4pm. And by
appointment.

9 STRATHSPEY GALLERY

40 High Street, Grantown-On Spey
PH26 3EH. Tel: 0479 873290.
Proprietors: Stephanie & James
Franses.
Quality antiques, mainly bought locally,
wildlife paintings and work by local
artists. H.A.D.A. member.
Open: 10am-1pm; 2pm-5pm weekdays
and Sat. Thurs: 10am-1pm.

6 MICHAEL LOW (ANTIQUES)

45 High Street, Forres, Morayshire
IV36 0PB.
Tel: 0309 673696.
Large selection of antique and Victorian
bric-a-brac, collectors items, pictures,
etc.
Mon-Sat: 10am-1pm; 2-5pm.

7 NAIRN ANTIQUES

St. Ninian Place, Nairn, Moray
IV12 4EQ.
Tel: 0667 53303.
Proprietor: Edwin D. Robertson.
Jewellery, silver, furniture, pottery,
porcelain, small permanent exhibition of
Scottish export pottery from S.E. Asia.
Mon-Sat: 9.30am-5pm. (Mon-Fri Lunch
Closure 1-2pm).

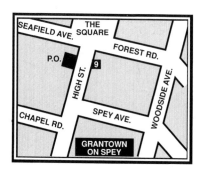

1 THE ATTIC

Riverside, 17 Huntly Street, Inverness IV3 5PR.
Tel: 0463 243117
Proprietor: P Gratton.
Victorian to Art Deco china, jewellery, period clothes and linen. Est. 1976. HADA member. Easy parking.
Mon-Sat: 10.30am-5pm. (Closed most Wednesdays).

2 FINDER'S CORNER

3 Muirfield Road, Inverness IV2 4AY.
Tel: 0463 231456 / 710346.
Eve: 0463 231456.
Proprietor: Mrs. Eve Bauchop.
Specialising in smalls; silver, glass, porcelain, furniture, jewellery. Trade welcome. Mostly circa 1900.
Car parking easy.
Mon-Fri: 1-7pm.

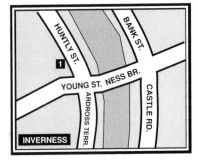

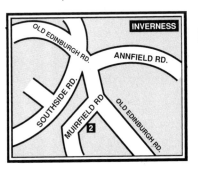

3 HIGHLAND ANTIQUES

Old Post Office, Avoch, Black Isle, Ross-shire.
Tel: 0381 621000. Eve: 772250.
Interesting general stock. Easy free parking. Member of HADA.
Mon-Sat: 10.30am-5pm. Closed Thu.

4 IAIN MARR ANTIQUES

3 Mid Street, Beauly, Inverness-shire IV4 7DP.
Tel: 0463 782372. Eve: 0463 83609.
Dealers in antique and Scottish provincial silver, weaponry, clocks, porcelain, glass, instruments and jewellery, since 1975. Member of HADA
Mon-Sat: 10.30am-1pm; 2-5.30pm. Closed Thu.

This index is designed to be used as a general guide to stock carried and services provided. Individual listings should be consulted for more detail on specialities and opening times etc.

ANTIQUES

Antiques/General

Antiques Centres

Antiques (Small)

Architectural Items

Art Nouveau/Deco

Art Nouveau/Deco Lamps

Barometers

Brass/Copper/Pewter

Brass Decorative Objects

Bric-a-Brac

Clocks

China/Porcelain/Glass/ Ceramics

Curios

Curiosities

FURNITURE

Antique Bedsteads (Brass, Brass/Iron, Wooden)

Antique/General

Antique/Reproduction

Carpets & Rugs

Garden Ornaments/Furniture

18th Century Furniture

Old Pine/Country Furniture

Oriental

Oriental Rugs & Carpets

COLLECTORS' ITEMS

114

Records

Scales & Balances

Scientific Instruments

Stamps

Treen

Vintage Watches

Vintage Projectors & Cine Cameras

Vintage Wireless Sets/Radios

GALLERIES

Contemporary Art

Contemporary Ceramics/ Glass

Contemporary Crafts

Contemporary Scottish Art

Contemporary Jewellery

Ethnic Art

Fine Art

20th Century Scottish Painters

18th/19th/20th Century Oils/ Watercolours

Paintings/Prints

Prints/Etchings/Engravings

Scottish Paintings

Sculpture

BOOKS

Antiquarian/Second Hand

Art Books

Collectors' Books

Children's Books

Film/TV/Sport/Pop

Golf Books

Islands/Topography

Literature

Naval & Maritime

Rare Books

Scottish Books

SPECIALIST SERVICES

Antique Furniture Restoration

Antique Restorers

Architectural Salvage

Auction Houses

Barometer Repair/Restoration

Clock/Watch Repairs/ Restoration

Cabinetmakers

Cane Work/Rush Seating

Chrome Stripping

Courier Service

Customer Services/Export/ Packing

French Polishers

Furniture & Antiques Restorer

Antique Furniture Repairs/ Restoration

Furniture Restoration Courses

Glass Restoration

Interior & Conservation Consultant

Upholsterers

Valuations

Vintage Wireless/Radio Repair & Restoration

Wood Carving

TEXTILES

Ethnic Textiles/Rugs

Linen & Lace

Oriental Clothing

Paisley Shawls & Quilts

Period Clothes/Accessories

Period Textiles/Fabrics

Samplers

Tapestries

JEWELLERY

Antique/Second-Hand

Costume Jewellery

Designer Jewellery

Ethnic/Tribal Jewellery

Scottish Jewellery

Alphabetical Index